# Observations *by* Mr. Dooley

# Observations
## *by* Mr. Dooley

GREENWOOD PRESS, PUBLISHERS
NEW YORK

Originally published in 1902
by R. H. Russell

First Greenwood Reprinting 1969

Library of Congress Catalogue Card Number 69-13889

SBN 8371-1636-8

PRINTED IN UNITED STATES OF AMERICA

# CONTENTS

[ v ]

# Contents

# A Little Essay on Books

# OBSERVATIONS
# By Mr. Dooley

## A LITTLE ESSAY
## ON BOOKS

"HOGAN tells me that wan iv th' first things man done afther he'd larned to kill his neighborin' animals, an' make a meal iv wan part iv thim an' a vest iv another, was to begin to mannyfacther lithrachoor, an' it's been goin' on up to th' prisint day. Thim was times that th' Lord niver heerd about, but is as well known to manny a la-ad in th' univarsity iv southren Injyanny as if th' histhry iv thim was printed on a poster. Hogan says a pro-fissor with a shovel an' a bad bringin'-up can go out annywhere along th' dhrainage-canal an' prove to ye that th' Bible is no more thin an exthry avenin' edition iv th' histhry iv th' wurruld, an' th' Noah fam'ly was considhered new arrivals in th' neighborhood where they lived. He says he'll show ye th' earth as though 't was a section iv a layer-cake or an archytect's dhrawin' iv a flat-buildin', an' p'int out how 't was accumylated.

" First 't was a mere squdge in which ne'er a livin'

[ 3 ]

thing cud be found. This peryod lasted a few millyion
years, an' thin th' mush caked an' become buildin'-
materyal, an' threes grew out iv th' buildin'-materyal
an' fell down an' become coal. Thin th' wather come
—but where it come fr'm I don't know, f'r they was
no God at th' time—an' covered th' earth, an' thin
th' wather evaporated an' left little p'ints iv land
shtickin' up with ready-made men an' women occy-
pyin' thim, an' at that moment th' Bible begun.
Ye might say we 're livin' on th' roof iv a flat,
with all th' apartmints beneath us occypied be th'
bones iv submarine monsthers an' other tinants.

"Lasteways that 's what Hogan tells me, but I don't
believe a wurrud he says. Most iv th' people iv this
wurruld is a come-on f'r science, but I'm not. Ye can't
con-vince me, me boy, that a man who's so near-sighted
he can't read th' sign on a cable-car knows anny more
about th' formation iv th' earth thin Father Kelly. I
believe th' wurruld is flat, not round; that th' sun
moves an' is about th' size iv a pie-plate in th' mornin'
an' a car-wheel at noon; an' it 's no proof to me that
because a pro-fissor who 's peekin' through a chube
all night says th' stars ar-re millyions iv miles away
an' each is bigger thin this wurruld, that they 're
bigger thin they look, or much higher thin th' top
iv th' shot-tower. I've been up tin thousand feet on
a mountain, an' they seemed so near that I kept
whiskin' thim off me nose as I lay there on me back,
but they wasn't anny larger thin they were on th'
sthreet-level. I believe what I see an' some iv th'
things I'm told, if they 've been told often, an' thim

[ 4 ]

facts iv science has not been hung long enough to be
digistible.

"But, annyhow, they say that man first begun writin' whin he had to hammer out his novels an' pomes on
a piece iv rock, an' th' hammer has been th' imblim iv
lithrachoor iver since. Thin he painted it on skins,
hince th' publisher; thin he played it an' danced it
an' croshayed it till 't was discovered that ink an'
pa-aper wud projooce wurruds, an' thin th' printin'-
press was invinted. Gunpowdher was invinted th' same
time, an' 't is a question I've often heerd discussed
which has done more to ilivate th' human race. A
joke.

" Th' longer th' wurruld lasts th' more books does
be comin' out. Day be day I r-read in th' pa-apers
announcemints iv new publications that look like th'
dilinquent tax-list. They 's a publisher in ivry block,
an' in thousan's iv happy homes some wan is pluggin'
away at th' romantic novel or whalin' out a pome on
th' type-writer up-stairs. A fam'ly without an author
is as contimptible as wan without a priest. Is Malachi
near-sighted, peevish, averse to th' suds, an' can't tell
whether th' three in th' front yard is blue or green?
Make an author iv him! Does Miranda prisint no
atthractions to th' young men iv th' neighborhood,
does her overskirt dhrag, an' is she poor with th' gas-
range? Make an authoreen iv her! Forchunitly,
th' manly insthinct is often too sthrong f'r th' designs
iv th' fam'ly, an' manny a man that if his parents had
had their way might have been at this moment makin'
artificial feet f'r a deformed pome is l'adin' what me

fri'nd Hogan calls a glad, free, an' timperymintal life
on th' back iv a sthreet-car.

" But lithrachoor is th' gr-reat life-wurruk iv th'
modhren woman. Th' conthrol is passin' into th'
hands iv th' fair sect, an' th' day will come whin th'
wurrud book will mane no more to an able-bodied man
thin th' wurrud gusset. Women write all th' romantic novels that ar-re anny good. That's because ivry
man thinks th' thrue hayroe is himsilf, an' ivry
woman thinks he's James K. Hackett. A woman is
sure a good, sthrong man ought to be able to kill
anny number iv bad, weak men, but a man is always
wondherin' what th' other la-ad wud do. He might
have th' punch left in him that wud get th' money.
A woman niver cares how manny men are kilt, but a
man believes in fair play, an' he 'd like to see th' polis
intherfere about Chapter Three.

" Women writes all th' good romantic novels, an'
read thim all. If anny proud la-ad in th' gum business thinks he riprisints th' ideal iv his wife's soul, he
ought to take a look at th' books she reads. He 'll
larn there th' reason he 's where he is, is because he was
th' on'y chanst, not because he was th' first choice.
'Twud humble th' haughtiest prince iv thrade to look
into th' heart iv th' woman he cares most f'r an' thinks
laste about, an' find that, instead iv th' photygraft
iv a shrewd but kindly man with a thriflin' absence iv
hair on his head an' a burglar-proof safe on his watch-
charm, there 's a pitcher iv a young la-ad in green
tights playin' a mandolin to a high front stoop. On
th' stoop, with a rose in her hand, is his lawful-wedded

[ 6 ]

wife, th' lady Annamariar Huggins iv Peotone. Ye can't keep her away fr'm a romantic novel. No matther what Edward Atkinson tells ye, she prefers ' Th' Age iv Chivalry' to th' mos' atthractive housewurruk. A woman's readin' is niver done. Hardly a day passes but some lady frind iv mine stops me on me way to catch a car, an' asks me if I don't regard Morse Hewlett as th' gr-reatest an' mos' homicidal writer iv our time, an' what I've got to say about Hinnelly's attack on Stevenson. ' Madam,' says I, ' I wud n't know Morse if I was to see him goin' down th' sthreet ax in hand, an' as f'r Hinnelly, his name escapes me, though his language is familiar to anny wan who iver helped load a scow. Stevenson,' I says, ' does n't appeal to me, an' if he shud, I 'll revarse th' decision on th' ground iv th' bad prevyous charackter iv th' plaintiff, while,' I says, ' admittin' th' thruth iv what he said. But,' says I, ' th' on'y books in me libr'y is th' Bible an' Shakspere,' says I. ' They 're gr-reat f'r ye,' says she. ' So bully f'r th' style. D' ye read thim all th' time?' she says. ' I niver read thim,' says I. ' I use thim f'r purposes iv definse. I have niver read thim, but I'll niver read annything else till I have read thim,' I says. ' They shtand between me an' all modhren lithrachoor,' says I. ' I 've built thim up into a kind iv breakwather,' I says, ' an' I set behind it ca'm an' contint while Hall Caine rages without,' says I.

"Yes, sir, th' readin' an' writin' iv books is as much woman's wurruk as th' mannyfacther iv tidies. A woman is a nachral writer. She don't mind givin'

hersilf away if 't will bring a tear to th' eye or a smile
to th' lips. But a man does. He has more to give
away. I 'm not sayin' that anny man can't write
betther thin a woman if he wants to. But so can he
cuk betther, an' sew betther, an' paint minichoors
betther, an' do annything betther but nurse th' baby—
if he wants to; but he don't often want to. He despises
such thrivyal pursuits. Mos' iv th' gr-reat writers
I iver see th' pitchers iv was little, thin, peevish men
that was always gettin' licked. Wanst in a while a
sthrong man got into th' game, a bull-necked, round-
headed man that might have made a fine thrackmaster
or boiler-maker, but was addicted to dhrink, an' niver
had energy enough left in th' mornin' f'r annything
more thin writin' th' best plays or th' finest novels or
th' gr-reatest histhries in th' wurruld. But if ye
got at th' rale feelin' iv three-meal-a-day men about
writin', ye 'd find they classed it with preachin', school-
teachin', play-actin', dancin', an' lace-wurruk. A man
iv that kind might start to write, but if he did, he 'd
stop an' think afther a while, an' say to himsilf:
' What 's a big, sthrong, able-bodied, two-hundhred-
an'-tin-pound, forty-four-acrost-th'-chest crather like
me doin' here, pokin' these funny hireyoglyphics into
a piece iv pa-aper with a little sthick? I guess I 'll go
out an' shoe a horse.'

"So it is with readin'. I 'm tol' I ought to read more
be Hogan, who 's wan iv th' best-read an' mos' ignorant men I know. Well, maybe I ought, though whin
I was a young man, an' was helpin' to build up this
counthry, th' principal use iv lithrachoor was as a

weepin. In thim days, if a little boy was seen readin'
a book, his father took it away fr'm him an' bate him
on th' head with it. Me father was th' mos' accyrate
man in th' wurruld with letthers. He found th' range
nachrally, an' he cud wing anny wan iv us with th'
'Lives iv th' Saints' as far as he cud see. He was
a poor man, an' on'y had such books in his libr'y as
a gintleman shud take, but if ye 'd give him libr'y
enough, he 'd capture Giberaltor. If lithrachoor niver
pinethrated me intelleck, 't was not his fault. But
nowadays, whin I go down th' sthreet, I see th' childher
settin' on th' front steps studyin' a book through
double-compound-convex spectacles, lookin' like th'
offspring of a pro-fissyonal diver. What 'll they iver
grow up to be? Be hivins! that la-ad Carnaygie
knows his business. He is studied th' situation, an'
he undhersthands that if he builds libr'ies enough
an' gets enough people readin' books, they won't be
anny wan left afther a while capable iv takin' away
what he 's got. Ye bet he did n't larn how to make
steel billets out iv 'Whin Knighthood was in Flower.'
He larned it be confabulatin' afther wurrukin' hours
with some wan that knew how. I think he must be
readin' now, f'r he 's writin' wan or two. 'T is th'
way with a man who takes to readin' late in life. He
can't keep it down.

"Readin', me frind, is talked about be all readin'
people as though it was th' on'y thing that makes a
man betther thin his neighbors. But th' thruth is
that readin' is th' nex' thing this side iv goin' to
bed f'r restin' th' mind. With mos' people it takes

th' place iv wurruk. A man does n't think whin he 's
readin', or if he has to, th' book is no fun. Did ye
iver have something to do that ye ought to do, but
did n't want to, an' while ye was wishin' ye was dead,
did ye happen to pick up a newspaper? Ye know
what occurred. Ye did n't jus' skim through th'
spoortin' intillygince an' th' crime news. Whin ye
got through with thim, ye read th' other quarther
iv th' pa-aper. Ye read about people ye niver heerd
iv, an' happenin's ye did n't undhersthand—th'
fashion notes, th' theatrical gossip, th' s'ciety news
fr'm Peoria, th' quotations on oats, th' curb market,
th' rale-estate transfers, th' marredge licenses, th'
death notices, th' want ads., th' dhrygoods bargains,
an' even th' iditoryals. Thin ye r-read thim over
again, with a faint idee ye 'd read thim befure. Thin
ye yawned, studied th' design iv th' carpet, an' settled
down to wurruk. Was ye exercisin' ye-er joynt intelleck while ye was readin'? No more thin if ye 'd
been whistlin' or writin' ye-er name on a pa-aper. If
anny wan else but me come along they might say:
' What a mind Hinnissy has! He 's always readin'.'
But I wud kick th' book or pa-aper out iv ye-er hand,
an' grab ye be th' collar, an' cry ' Up, Hinnissy, an'
to wurruk!' f'r I 'd know ye were loafin'. Believe
me, Hinnissy, readin' is not thinkin'. It seems like it,
an' whin it comes out in talk sometimes, it sounds like
it. It 's a kind iv nearthought that looks ginooine
to th' thoughtless, but ye can't get annything on it.
Manny a man I 've knowed has so doped himsilf
with books that he 'd stumble over a carpet-tack.

## A Little Essay on Books

"Am I again' all books, says ye? I 'm not. If I had money, I 'd have all th' good lithrachoor iv th' wurruld on me table at this minyit. I might n't read it, but there it 'd be so that anny iv me fri'nds cud dhrop in an' help thimsilves if they did n't care f'r other stimylants. I have no taste f'r readin', but I won't deny it 's a good thing f'r thim that 's addicted to it. In modheration, mind ye. In modheration, an' afther th' chores is done. F'r as a frind iv Hogan's says, ' Much readin' makes a full man,' an' he knew what he was talkin' about. An' do I object to th' pursuit iv lithrachoor? Oh, faith, no. As a pursuit 't is fine, but it may be bad f'r anny wan that catches it."

# The Law's Delays

"IF I had me job to pick out," said Mr. Dooley, "I'd be a judge. I've looked over all th' others an' that's th' on'y wan that suits. I have th' judicyal timperamint. I hate wurruk.

"Ivrybody else is pushed an' hurrid in this tumulchuse age. Th' business man has to get to th' bank befure it closes an' th' banker has to get there befure th' business man escapes, an' th' high-priced actor has to kill off more gradyates iv th' school iv actin' thin iver he did, an' th' night editions iv th' pa-apers comes out arlier ivry mornin'. All is rush an' worry. Kings an' imprors duck about their jooties like bell-hops, th' pampered son iv luxury at Newport is thryin' f'r a mile a minyit in his autymobill an' th' on'y leisure class left in th' wurruld is th' judicyary. Mind ye, Hinnissy, I'm not sayin' annything again' thim. I won't dhrag th' joodicyal ermine in th' mud though I haven't noticed that manny iv thim lift it immodestly whin they takes th' pollytical crossing. I have th' high rayspict f'r th' job that's th' alternative iv sixty days in jail. Besides, me boy, I invy thim.

"Somewhere a la-ad hits somewan on th' head with an axe or sinds him a bunch iv proosic acid done up to look like candy. Maybe he does an' maybe he don't; but annyhow that's what he's lagged f'r. Th' polis

are in a hurry to get to th' pool-room befure th' flag
falls in th' first race an' they carry th' case to th' gran'
jury; th' gran' jury indicts him without a thought or
a suspicion iv a har-rd feelin', th' judge takes his
breakfast on th' bench to be there in time an' charges
th' jury to be fair but not to f'rget th' man done it,
an' th' jury rayturns a verdict iv guilty with three
cheers an' a tiger. Th' pris'ner has hardly time to
grab up his hat befure he's hauled off to his funeral
obsequies, an' th' onprejudiced public feels happy
about it. I don't believe in capital punishmint,
Hinnissy, but 'twill niver be abolished while th' people
injye it so much. They're jus' squarin' thimsilves f'r
th' rayvoltin' details whin wurrud comes that Judge
Tamarack iv Opolis has granted a stay iv proceedin's.
Stays iv pro-ceedin's is devices, Hinnissy, be which
th' high coorts keep in form. 'Tis a lagal joke. I
med it up. Says Judge Tamarack: ' I know very
little about this case excipt what I've been tol' be th'
larned counsel f'r th' dayfinse, an' I don't believe that,
but I agree with Lord Coke in th' maxim that th'
more haste th' less sleep. Therefore to all sheriffs,
greetin': Fen jarrin' th' pris'ner till ye hear fr'm
us.'

" So th' pris'ner waits an' dhreams he's a lightnin'
rod an' th' public waits an' ivrybody waits. Th' high
coort is busy in its way. Ivry two or three years it is
discovered takin' a nap at a county seat in th' corn
belt, an' it hands down a decision f'r th' defindant in
a case f'r damages growin' out iv th' Shay rebillion.
Then it dhrops off again. Th' judge that thried th'

case retires to a well-arned job with a railrood com-
p'ny, th' jury has ceased to look f'r their pitchers in
th' pa-apers an' th' insurance comp'nies insure young
Cyanide's life f'r the lowest known premyum. Occasionally a judge iv th' coort iv appeals walkin' in
his sleep meets another judge, an' they discuss matthers. ' How ar-re ye gettin' on with th' Cyanide
case, judge? ' ' I 'm makin' fair headway, judge.
I r-read part iv th' vardict iv th' coroner's jury las'
year an' nex' month whin th' fishin' is over, I expict
to look into th' indictment. 'Tis a puzzlin' case.
Th' man is not guilty.' ' Well, good bye, judge; I'll
see ye in a year or two. Lave me know how ye're
gettin' on. Pleasant dhreams! ' An' so they part.
Th' higher up a coort is, th' less they see iv each other.
Their office hours are fr'm a quarther to wan leap
years. Ye take a lively lawyer that 's wurruked twinty
hours a day suin' sthreet railrood comp'nies an' boost
him onto a high coort an' he can't think out iv a
hammock. Th' more exalted what Hogan calls th'
joodicyal station, th' more it's like a dormitory. Th'
years rowl by an' th' tillygraft op'rator that's been
expictin' to sind a rush tillygram through young
Cyanide sees his ohms an' his volts mouldin' an' no
wurrud comes fr'm th' coort iv appeals but th' murmur
iv th' chief justice discussin' th' nullification theery.
But wan day, th' decision is wafted down. ' Th'
coort finds,' it says, ' that th' vardict was conthry to
th' law an' th' ividince. We seen this fr'm th' first.
It's as plain as th' nose on ye'er face. Th' judge was
prejudiced an' th' jury was ignorant. Th' ividince

wasn't sufficient to hang a cat. We revarse th' decision an' ordher a new thrile that full justice may be done. We cannot help remarkin' at this time on th' croolty iv subjectin' this unforchnit man to all these years iv torture an' imprisonment with a case again' him which we see at a glance durin' th' Mexican war cud not shtand th' test iv th' law.'

"But whin th' decision is carried to th' pris'ner, th' warden says 'Who?' 'P. Cyanide,' says th' clark iv th' coort. 'He's not here,' says th' warden. 'On consultin' me books, I find a man iv that name left in th' year sivinty-wan.' 'Did he escape?' 'In a sinse. He's dead.'

"So, Hinnissy, I'd like to be a judge iv a high coort, dhreamin' th' happy hours away. No hurry, no sthrivin' afther immejet raysults, no sprintin', no wan hollerin' 'Dooley J. hurry up with that ne exeat,' or 'Dooley, hand down that opinyion befure th' batthry gives out.' 'Tis th' thrue life iv aise an' gintlemanly comfort. 'Tis wait till th' clouds rowl by; 'tis time was meant for slaves; 'tis a long life an' a happy wan. Like th' Shamrock II, th' coort acts well in stays but can't run befure th' wind. A jury is f'r hangin' ivry man, but th' high coort says: 'Ye must die, but take ye'er time about it an' go out th' way ye like.' If I wanted to keep me money so that me gran'-childher might get it f'r their ol' age, I'd appeal it to th' supreme coort. Oh, th' fine judge I'd make, f'r I can sleep annywhere, an' I'm niver impatient f'r annywan to get his jooes."

"I don't see," said Mr. Hennessy, "why they have

anny juries. Why don't they thry ivry man before th' supreme coort an' have done with it?"

"I have a betther way than that," said Mr. Dooley. "Ye see they 're wurrukin' on time now. I wondher if they wudden't sthep livelier if they were paid be th' piece."

# Sherlock Holmes

"**D**ORSEY an' Dugan are havin' throuble," said Mr. Hennessy.

"What about?" asked Mr. Dooley.

"Dorsey," said Mr. Hennessy, "says Dugan stole his dog. They had a party at Dorsey's an' Dorsey heerd a noise in th' back yard an' wint out an' see Dugan makin' off with his bull tarryer."

"Ye say he see him do it?"

"Yis, he see him do it."

"Well," said Mr. Dooley, "'twud baffle th' injinooty iv a Sherlock Holmes."

"Who's Sherlock Holmes?"

"He's th' gr-reatest detictive that iver was in a story book. I've been r-readin' about him an' if I was a criminal, which I wud be if I had to wurruk f'r a livin', an' Sherlock Holmes got afther me, I'd go sthraight to th' station an' give mesilf up. I'd lay th' goods on th' desk an' say: ' Sargeant, put me down in th' hard cage. Sherlock Holmes has jus' see a man go by in a cab with a Newfoundland dog an' he knows I took th' spoons.' Ye see, he ain't th' ordh'nry fly cop like Mulcahy that always runs in th' Schmidt boy f'r ivry crime rayported fr'm stealin' a ham to forgin' a check in th' full knowledge that some day he'll get him f'r th' right thing. No, sir; he's an injanyous man that can put two an' two together an' make eight iv thim. He applies his brain to crime, d'ye mind, an' divvle th' crime, no matther how cunnin' it is, will escape him. We'll suppose, Hinnissy, that I'm Sherlock Holmes. I'm settin' here in me little parlor wearin' a dhressin' gown an' now an' thin pokin' mesilf full iv morpheen. Here we are. Ye come in. ' Good-mornin', Watson.' "

" I ain't Watson," said Mr. Hennessy. " I'm Hinnissy."

" Ah," said Mr. Dooley; " I thought I'd wring it fr'm ye. Perhaps ye'd like to know how I guessed ye had come in. 'Tis very simple. On'y a matther iv observation. I heerd ye'er step; I seen ye'er refliction in th' lookin' glass; ye spoke to me. I put these things together with me thrained faculty f'r observation an' deduction, d'ye mind. Says I to mesilf : ' This must be Hinnissy.' But mind ye, th' chain iv circumstances is not complete. It might be some wan disguised as ye. So says I to mesilf : ' I will throw this newcome, who-iver he is, off his guard, be callin' him be a sthrange name !' Ye wudden't feel complimented, Hinnissy, if ye knew who Watson is. Watson knows even less than ye do. He don't know annything, an' anny-thing he knows is wrong. He has to look up his name in th' parish raygisther befure he can speak to himsilf. He's a gr-reat frind iv Sherlock Holmes an' if Sherlock Holmes iver loses him, he'll find him in th' nearest asylum f'r th' feeble-minded. But I sur-prised ye'er secret out iv ye. Thrown off ye'er guard be me innocent question, ye popped out 'I'm Hinnissy,' an' in a flash I guessed who ye were. Be th' same process iv raisonin' be deduction, I can tell ye that ye were home las' night in bed, that ye're on ye'er way to wurruk, an' that ye'er salary is two dollars a day. I know ye were at home las' night because ye ar-re always at home between iliven an' sivin, bar Pathrick's night, an' ye'er wife hasn't been in lookin' f'r ye. I know ye're on ye'er way to wurruk because I heerd ye'er dinner pail jingle as ye stepped softly in. I know ye get two dollars a day because ye tol' me ye get three an' I deducted thirty-three an' wan third per cint f'r poetic license. 'Tis very simple. Ar-re those shoes ye have on ye'er feet? Be hivins, I thought so."

"Simple," said Mr. Hennessy, scornfully; "'tis foolish."

"Niver mind," said Mr. Dooley. "Pass th' dope, Watson. Now bein' full iv th' cillybrated Chow Sooey brand, I addhress me keen mind to th' discussion iv th' case iv Dorsey's dog. Watson, look out iv th' window an' see if that's a cab goin' by ringin' a gong. A throlley car? So much th' betther. Me observation tol' me it was not a balloon or a comet or a reindeer. Ye ar-re a gr-reat help to me, Watson. Pass th' dope. Was there a dog on th' car? No? That simplifies th' thing. I had an idee th' dog might have gone to wurruk. He was a bull-tarryer, ye say. D'ye know annything about his parents? Be Mulligan's Sloppy Weather out iv O'Hannigan's Diana iv th' Slough? Iv coorse. Was ayether iv thim seen in th' neighborhood th' night iv th' plant? No? Thin it is not, as manny might suppose, a case iv abduction. What were th' habits iv Dorsey's coyote? Was he a dog

[ 25 ]

that dhrank? Did he go out iv nights? Was he payin'
anny particular attintions to anny iv th' neighbors?
Was he baffled in love? Ar-re his accounts sthraight?
Had Dorsey said annything to him that wud 've made
him despondent? Ye say no. He led a dog's life but
seemed to be happy. Thin 'tis plainly not a case iv
suicide.

"I'm gettin' up close to th' criminals. Another
shot iv th' mad mixture. Wait till I can find a place
in th' ar-rm. There ye ar-re. Well, Watson, what
d'ye make iv it?"

"If ye mane me, Dugan stole th' dog."

"Not so fast," said Mr. Dooley. "Like all men
iv small minds ye make ye'ers up readily. Th' smaller
th' mind, th' aisier 'tis made up. Ye'ers is like a
blanket on th' flure befure th' fire. All ye have to do
to make it up is to lave it. Mine is like a large double
bed, an' afther I've been tossin' in it, 'tis no aisy job
to make it up. I will puncture me tire with th' fav'rite
flower iv Chinnytown an' go on. We know now that
th' dog did not elope, that he didn't commit suicide an'
that he was not kidnaped be his rayturnin' parents.
So far so good. Now I'll tell ye who stole th' dog.
Yisterdah afthernoon I see a suspicious lookin' man
goin' down th' sthreet. I say he was suspicious lookin'
because he was not disguised an' looked ivry wan in
th' face. He had no dog with him. A damning cir-
cumstance, Watson, because whin he'd stolen th' dog
he niver wud 've taken it down near Dorsey's house.
Ye wudden't notice these facts because ye'er mind
while feeble is unthrained. His coat collar was turned

up an' he was whistlin' to himsilf, a habit iv dog
fanciers. As he wint be Hogan's house he did not look
around or change his gait or otherwise do annything
that wud indicate to an unthrained mind that there
was annything wrong, facts in thimsilves that proved
to me cultivated intilligence that he was guilty. I
followed him in me mind's eye to his home an' there
chained to th' bed leg is Dorsey's dog. Th' name iv
th' criminal is P. X. O'Hannigan, an' he lives at
twinty-wan hundhred an' ninety-nine South Halsted
sthreet, top flat, rear, a plumber be pro-fission. Officer, arrest that man!"

"That's all right," said Mr. Hennessy; "but
Dugan rayturned th' dog las' night."

"Oh, thin," said Mr. Dooley, calmly, "this is not
a case f'r Sherlock Holmes but wan f'r th' polis.
That's th' throuble, Hinnissy, with th' detective iv th'
story. Nawthin' happens in rale life that's compli-
cated enough f'r him. If th' Prisidint iv th' Epworth
League was a safe-blower be night th' man that'd
catch him'd be a la-ad with gr-reat powers iv observation an' thrained habits iv raisonin'. But crime, Hinnissy, is a pursoot iv th' simple minded—that is,
catchable crime is a pursoot iv th' simple-minded. Th'
other kind, th' uncatchable kind that is took up be
men iv intellict is called high fi-nance. I've known
manny criminals in me time, an' some iv thim was fine
men an' very happy in their home life, an' a more
simple, pasth'ral people ye niver knew. Wan iv th'
ablest bank robbers in th' counthry used to live near
me—he ownded a flat buildin'—an' befure he'd turn

[ 27 ]

**in** to bed afther rayturnin' fr'm his night's wurruk, he'd go out in th' shed an' chop th' wood. He always wint into th' house through a thransom f'r fear iv wakin' his wife who was a delicate woman an' a shop lifter. As I tell ye he was a man without guile, an' he wint about his jooties as modestly as ye go about ye'ers. I don't think in th' long run he made much more thin ye do. Wanst in a while, he'd get hold iv a good bunch iv money, but manny other times afther dhrillin' all night through a steel dure, all he'd find 'd be a short crisp note fr'm th' prisidint iv th' bank. He was often discouraged, an' he tol' me wanst if he had an income iv forty dollars th' month, he'd retire fr'm business an' settle down on a farm.

" No, sir, criminals is th' simplest crathers in th' wide wide wurruld—innocent, sthraight-forward, dangerous people, that haven't sinse enough to be honest or prosperous. Th' extint iv their schamin' is to break a lock on a dure or sweep a handful iv change fr'm a counter or dhrill a hole in a safe or administher th' strong short arm to a tired man takin' home his load. There are no mysteryous crimes excipt thim that happens to be. Th' ordh'nry crook, Hinnissy, goes around ringin' a bell an' disthributin' hand-bills announcin' his business. He always breaks through a window instead iv goin' through an open dure, an' afther he's done annything that he thinks is commindable, he goes to a neighborin' liquor saloon, stands on th' pool table an' confides th' secret to ivrybody within sound iv his voice. That's why Mulligan is a betther detictive thin Sherlock Holmes or me. He can't put two an' two together an' he has no powers iv deduction, but he's a hard dhrinker an' a fine sleuth. Sherlock Holmes niver wud've caught that frind iv mine. Whin th' safe iv th' Ninth Rational Bank was blowed, he wud've put two an' two together an' arristed me. But me frind wint away lavin' a hat an' a pair iv cuffs marked with his name in th' safe, an' th' polis combined these discoveries with th' well-known fact that Muggins was a notoryous safe blower an' they took him in. They found him down th' sthreet thryin' to sell a bushel basket full iv Alley L stock. I told ye he was a simple man. He ralized his ambition f'r an agaracoolchral life. They give him th' care iv th' cows at Joliet."

" Did he rayform? " asked Mr. Hennessy.

" No," said Mr. Dooley; " he escaped. An' th' way he got out wud baffle th' injinooty iv a Sherlock Holmes."

" How did he do it? " asked Mr. Hennessy.

" He climbed over th' wall," said Mr. Dooley.

# International Amenities

" BE hivins," said Mr. Dooley, "I wisht I'd been there."

"Where?" asked Mr. Hennessy.

" At th' bankit iv th' Ancyent an' Hon'rable Chamber iv Commerce in New York," said Mr. Dooley. " 'Tis a hard fate that compels me to live out here on th' prairies among th' aborig'nal Americans fr'm Poland an' Bohaymya. Me heart at times is burstin' f'r to jine in th' festivities iv me fellow Britons in New York. F'r I'm a British subjick, Hinnissy. I wasn't born wan. I was born in Ireland. But I have a little money put away, an' ivry American that has larned to make wan dollar sthick to another is ex-officio, as Hogan says, a British subjick. We've adopted a foster father. Some iv us ain't anny too kind to th' ol' gintleman. In th' matther iv th' Nicaragoon Canal we have recently pushed him over an' took about all he had. But our hearts feels th' love iv th' parent counthry, though our hands is rebellyous, an' ivry year me fellow-merchants gets together in New York an' f'rgets th' cares iv th' wool an' tallow business in an outburst iv devotion to th' ol' land fr'm which our fathers sprung or was sprung be th' authorities.

" Th' prisidint iv th' bankit was me frind Morse K. Cheeseshop a mimber iv an ol' Yorkshire fam'ly born in th' West Riding iv Long Island befure th'

Crimeyan War. At his right sat th' Sicrety iv state f'r th' colony, an' at his left me frind th' ambassadure to th' Coort iv Saint James. Why we shud sind an ambassadure I don't know, though it may be an ol' custom kept up f'r to plaze th' people iv Omaha. He's a good man, th' ambassadure, who is inthra- joocin' th' American joke in England. Hogan says th' diff'rence between an American joke an' an Eng- lish joke is th' place to laugh. In an American joke ye laugh just afther th' point if at all, but in an English joke ye laugh ayether befure th' point or afther th' decease iv th' joker. Th' ambassadure hopes to inthrajooce a cross iv th' two that ye don't laugh at at all that will be suited to th' English mar- ket. His expeeriments so far has been encouragin'.

" At th' conclusion iv th' eatin' th' chairman, Sir Morse Cheeseshop inthrajooced th' sicrety iv state in a few well chosen wurruds. ' Fellow Colonists,' says he, ' I desire to presint His Majesty's ripresent- ative in this counthry who is doin' more thin anny other man in ' th' plastherin' business,' he says. ' Owin',' he says, ' to mimbers iv th' Sinit lavin' a hod iv bricks fall on his head recently, he has not been able to do much on th' job,' he says. ' But he has brought his throwel and morthar here to-night an' if ye will kindly lave off singing' " Brittanya rules th' prosperity wave " f'r a minyit he'll give ye an exhibi- tion iv how he wurruks. Me Lords an' gintlemen, th' sicrety iv state : '

" ' Fellow subjicks,' says th' sicrety iv state, ' diplomacy is far diff'rent business thin it used to be.

## International Amenities

(A voice, ' Good f'r you.') In th' days iv Bismarck, Gladstun an' Charles Francis Adams 'twas a case iv inthrigue an' deceit. Now it is as simple as sellin' a pair iv boots. In fifteen years th' whole nature iv man is so changed that a diplomat has on'y to be honest, straight-forward an' manly an' concede ivrything an' he will find his opponents will meet him half way an' take what he gives. Unforchunitly diplomacy on'y goes as far as the dure. It is onable to give protection to th' customer, so whin he laves th' shop th' sthrong arm men iv th' Sinit knocks him down an' takes fr'm him ivrything he got inside an' more too. Di-plomacy has become a philanthropic pursoot like shop-keepin', but politics, me lords, is still th' same ol' spoort iv highway robb'ry. But I done what I cud to protict th' intherests iv th' mother, father an' brother-in-law counthry, an' between you an' me if I don't desarve th' Victorya cross f'r presintin' that threaty to th' Sinit nobody does. I will on'y say that hinceforth th' policy iv this gover'mint will be as befure not to bully a sthrong power or wrong a weak, but will remain thrue to th' principle iv wrongin' th' sthrong an' bullyin' th' weak.'

" Th' sicrety iv state was followed be th' ambassadure. ' I wish to tell ye,' said he, ' what a good time I had in England. Befure I wint there I was sthrongly prejudiced again' England. I thought it was th' noblest counthry on which, as Dan'l Webster says, th' sun niver set without hatchin' out a new colony. But I did it a great injustice. It is betther thin what I thought. It does not care f'r chaff or

gush such as goes down in this counthry. All an
English gintleman demands is that ye shall be ye'ersilf, frank, manly an' sincere. A little cry on th'
shouldher, a firm grasp iv th' hand, a brief acknowl-
edgment that we owe our language an' are payin'
it back, our lithrachoor an' our boots to him, an' his
heart opens. He cannot conceal his admiration f'r
ye. He goes away. Ah, niver will I f'rget th' day
I peeked out iv me bed-room window at Windsor
Castle an' see manny iv th' sturdy lielists here befure
me bein' received in th' back yard be th' king. I
mind well th' wurruds that fell fr'm his lips whin ye
left to take lunch in th' rile woodshed. " Chote," he
says, " thim were a fine lot iv Americans," he says.
" What thribe did ye say they belonged to? Soos? "
he says.'

" So th' avenin' proceeded until it was time to go
home, whin th' chairman proposed th' customary
toast. ' Me lords an' gintlemen, charge ye'er glasses
an' jine me in a toast,' he says. ' His majesty Edward th' Sivinth, iv Gr-reat Britain an' possibly Ireland, iv Inja, Egypt, iv Austhralya, iv South Africa
in a sinse, an' iv th' Dominions beyant th' sea, includin' New York, King, Definder iv th' Faith. I
hope I got it all in.' ' Ye did,' said th' ambassadure.
An' th' toast was dhrunk with enthusyasm. Other
toasts was dhrunk to th' rile fam'ly an' th' Protestant
Succession, to th' Jook iv Argyle who used to own
Andhrew Carnaygie, an' in manny cases th' rile mer-
chants carrid th' glasses away in their pockets.
Jus' as th' comp'ny was breakin' up a man whose

gaiters creaked rose an' said: ' Isn't there wan more toast?' ' Good hivins have I f'rgotten somewan?' said Lord Cheeseshop. ' That was all there was in th' book. Who d'ye mane?' he says. ' I mane th' prisidint iv th' United States,' says th' man, who comes fr'm Baraboo. ' Oh him,' says th' chairman in a relieved tone. ' Well, annywan that wants to can dhrink his health at th' bar,' he says.

" As th' comp'ny filed out a band was playin' in th' adjinin' room where they was a meetin' iv th' Amalgamated Stove-polish men fr'm th' neighborhood iv Terry Hut. ' What 's that outlandish chune?' says Lord Cheeseshop. ' 'Tis th' naytional air, west iv Hoboken,' says th' man fr'm Baraboo. ' What 's it called?' says Lord Cheeseshop. ' Th' Star Spangled Banner,' says th' man. ' Well,' says Lord Cheeseshop, ' 'tis very intherestin',' he says. ' 'Tis th' on'y Indyan music I iver heerd,' he says."

" Ah well," said Mr. Hennessy, " who cares? "

" Faith I think ye're right," said Mr. Dooley. " A man will swallow annything with a dinner. What is good f'r what Hogan calls th' iliminthry canal has nawthin' to do with th' Nicaragoon Canal an' I'd be more afraid iv Lord Cheeseshop if he thought th' toast an' didn't say it. Our Anglo-Saxon relations is always a give-away—on some wan."

# Art Patronage

"I SEE in this pa-aper," said Mr. Dooley, "they'se a fellow kickin' because an American painther ain't got anny chanst again' foreign compytition."

"Sure," said Mr. Hennessy; "he's aisy displazed. I niver knew th' business to be betther. Wages is high an' 'tis a comfortable thrade barrin' colic."

"I don't mane that kind iv painthers," said Mr. Dooley. "I don't mane th' wans that paint ye'er barn, but th' wans that paints a pitcher iv ye'er barn an' wants to sell it to ye f'r more thin th' barn is worth. This man says no matther how industhrees an American painther is, no matther if he puts on his overalls arly in th' mornin' an' goes out with a laddher an' whales away all day long, he can hardly arn a livin', while th' pauper artists iv Europe is fairly rowlin' in th' lap iv luxury. Manny a la-ad that started in life with th' intintion iv makin' th' wurruld f'rget that what's his name—Hogan's frind —ye know who I mane—Michael Angelo—ever lived, is now glad to get a job decoratin' mountain scenery with th' latest news about th' little liver pills.

"Ye see, Hinnissy, whin a man gets hold iv a large hatful iv money, wan iv th' first things he does is to buy some art. Up to th' time whin th' top blew off th' stock market, he bought his art out

iv th' front window iv a news an' station'ry shop
or had it put in be th' paperhanger. He took th'
Sundah pa-apers that ar-re a gr-reat help if ye're
collectin' art, an' he had some pitchers iv fruit that
looks nachral enough to ate, d'ye mind, a paintin'
iv a deer like th' wan he shot at in th' Manotowish
counthry in Eighty-eight, an' a livin' likeness iv a
Lake Supeeryor white fish on a silver plate. That
was th' peeryod, mind ye, whin th' iron dogs howled
on his lawn an' people come miles an' miles f'r to
see a grotto made out iv relics iv th' Chicago fire.

" Manetime his daughter was illustratin' suspinders
an' illuminatin' china plates an' becomin' artistic, an'
afther awhile whin th' time come that he had to
keep a man at th' dure to sweep out th' small bills,
she give him a good push to'rd betther things. Besides, his pardner down th' sthreet had begun collectin' pitchers, an' ivry time he wint abroad th'
mannyfacthrers iv pitcher frames bought new auty-
mobills f'r th' Champs All Easy. So 'twas a soft
matther f'r our frind Higbie to be persuaded that
he ought to be a pathron iv art, an' he wint abroad
detarmined to buy a bunch iv chromos that'd make
people come out iv th' gallery iv his pardner down
th' sthreet stiflin' their laughter in their hands.

" Now ye'd think seein' that he made his money in
this counthry, he'd pathronize American art. Ye'd
believe he'd sind wurrud down to his agent f'r to
secure forty feet iv Evansville be moonlight an' be
con-tint. But he don't.

" Ye don't catch Higbie changin' iv anny iv his

[ 42 ]

dividends on domestic finished art. He jumps on a
boat an' goes sthraight acrost to th' centhral deepo.
The first thing he gets is a porthrait iv himsilf be
wan iv th' gr-reat modhren masthers, Sargent be
name. This here Sargent, Hogan tells me, used to
live in this counthry, an' faith, if he'd stayed here
ye might see him to-day on a stagin'. But he had
a mind in his head an' he tore off f'r Europe th'
way a duck hunter goes f'r a rice swamp. Afther
awhile, Higbie shows up, an' says he: ' I'm Higbie
iv th' Non-Adhesive Consolidated Glue Company,'
he says. ' Can ye do me? ' ' I can an' will,' says
Sargent. ' I'll do ye good. How much have ye
got? ' he says. ' Get some more an' come around,'
he says. An' Higbie puts on his Prince Albert coat
an' laves it open so that ye can see his watch charm—
th' crown iv Poland with th' Kohinoor in th' top iv it
—an' me frind Sargent does him brown an' red.
He don't give him th' pitcher iv coorse. If ye have
ye'er porthrait painted be a gr-reat painther, it's
ye'er porthrait but 'tis his pitcher, an' he keeps it
till ye don't look that way anny more. So Higbie's
porthrait is hung up in a gallery an' th' doctors
brings people to see it that ar-re sufferin' fr'm nar-
vous dyspepsia to cheer thim up. Th' pa-apers says
'tis fine. ' Number 108 shows Sargent at his best.
There is the same marvellous ticknick that th' great
master displayed in his cillybrated take-off on Mrs.
Maenheimer in last year's gallery. Th' skill an' ease
with which th' painther has made a monkey iv his
victim are beyond praise. Sargent has torn th'

sordid heart out iv th' wretched crather an' exposed it to th' wurruld. Th' wicked, ugly little eyes, th' crooked nose, th' huge graspin' hands, tell th' story iv this miscreant's character as completely as if they were written in so manny wurruds, while th' artist, with wondherful malice, has painted onto th' face a smile iv sickenin' silf-complacency that is positively disgustin'. No artist iv our day has succeeded so well in showin' up th' maneness iv th' people he has mugged. We ondershtand that th' atrocious Higbie paid wan hundherd thousan' dollars f'r this comic valentine. It is worth th' money to ivrybody but him.'

"But Higbie don't see th' pa-aper. He's over in Paris. Th' chimes are rung, bonefires are lighted in th' sthreets an' th' Pannyma Comp'ny declares a dividend whin he enters th' city. They'se such a demand f'r paint that th' supply runs out an' manny gr-reat imprishonist pitcher facthries is foorced to use bluein'. Higbie ordhers paintin's be th' ton, th' r-runnin' foot, th' foot pound, th' car load. He insthructs th' pitcher facthries to wurruk night an' day till his artistic sowl is satisfied. We follow his coorse in th' pa-apers. ' Th' cillybrated Gainsborough that niver wud be missed has been capt-ured be Misther Higbie, th' American millyionaire. Th' price paid is said to be wan hundherd thousan' dollars. Th' pitcher riprisints a lady in a large hat fondlin' a cow. It is wan iv th' finest Gainsboroughs painted be th' Gainsborough Mannyfacthrin' comp'ny iv Manchester. At th' las' public sale, it was sold f'r thirty dollars. Misther Higbie has also purchased th' cillybrated Schmartzmeister Boogooroo, wan iv th' mos' horrible examples iv this delightful painther's style. He is now negotyatin' with th' well-known dealer Moosoo Mortheimer f'r th' intire output iv th' Barabazah School. Yisterdah in a call on th' janial dealer, th' name iv th' cillybrated painther Mooney was mintioned. "How manny pitchers has he painted?" "Four hundherd and forty-three thousan' at ilivin o'clock to-day," says th' dealer. "But four hundherd thousan' iv thim ar-re in America." "Get th' r-rest iv thim f'r me," says th' connysoor. "What did ye say th' gintleman's name was?" We ondershtand that Misther Mooney has had to put in two new four-deck machines to meet th' ordhers, which include thirty green an' mauve haystacks, forty blue barns or childher at play, an' no less thin ninety riprisintations iv mornin' at sea, moonlight avenin', flock iv sheep, or whativer ye may call thim.'

"An' whin he comes home, he hangs thim in his house, so that his frinds can't turn around without takin' off a pasthral scene on their coats, an' he pastes th' price on th' frame, an' whin he dies, he laves his pitcher to some definceless art museem. An' there ye ar-re.

"So I tell ye, Hinnissy, if I was a young an' ambitious American painther, I'd go to Europe. Whin Hannigan was over there, he met a young man that painted that fine head iv Murphy that looks so much like Casey that hangs in Schwartzmeister's back room. 'Ar-re ye still at th' art?' says Hannigan.

'I am,' says th' young man. 'How does it go?' asks Hannigan. 'I've more thin I can do,' says th' young man. 'Since steel rails got so high, I've had to hire an assistant. Ye see, I didn't get on in Chicago. Me "Bridgepoort in a Fog" was th' on'y pitcher I sold, an' a sausage mannyfacthrer bought that because his facthry was in it. I come over here, an' so's me pitchers will have a fair show, I sign annywan's name ye want to thim. Ye've heerd iv Michael Angelo? That's me. Ye've heerd iv Gainsborough? That's me. Ye've heerd iv Millet, th' boy that painted th' pitcher give away with th' colored supplimint iv th' Sundah Howl? That's me. Yis, sir, th' rale name iv near ivry distinguished painther iv modhren times is Remsen K. Smith. Whin ye go home, if ye see a good painther an' glazier that'd like a job as assistant Rimbrandt f'r th' American thrade, sind him to me. F'r,' he says, 'th' on'y place an American artist can make a livin' is here. Charity f'r artists,' he says, 'begins abroad,' he says."

"Well," said Mr. Hennessy, "perhaps a bum Europeen pitcher is betther thin a good American pitcher."

"Perhaps so," said Mr. Dooley. "I think it is so. Annyhow, no matther how bad a painther he is, annywan that can get money out iv an American millyionaire is an artist an' desarves it. There's th' rale art. I wish it was taught in th' schools. I'd like to see an exhibition at th' Museem with 'Check iv American Gintleman, dhrawn fr'm life,' hung on th' wall."

# Immigration

"WELL, I see Congress has got to wurruk again," said Mr. Dooley.

"The Lord save us fr'm harm," said Mr. Hennessy.

"Yes, sir," said Mr. Dooley, "Congress has got to wurruk again, an' manny things that seems important to a Congressman 'll be brought up befure thim. 'Tis sthrange that what's a big thing to a man in Wash'nton, Hinnissy, don't seem much account to me. Divvle a bit do I care whether they dig th' Nicaragoon Canal or cross th' Isthmus in a balloon; or whether th' Monroe docthrine is enfoorced or whether it ain't; or whether th' thrusts is abolished as Teddy Rosenfelt wud like to have thim or encouraged to go on with their neefaryous but magnificent entherprises as th' Prisidint wud like; or whether th' water is poured into th' ditches to reclaim th' arid lands iv th' West or th' money f'r thim to fertilize th' arid pocket-books iv th' conthractors; or whether th' Injun is threated like a depindant an' miserable thribesman or like a free an' indepindant dog; or whether we restore th' merchant marine to th' ocean or whether we lave it to restore itsilf. None iv these here questions inthrests me, an' be me I mane you an' be you I mane ivrybody. What we want to know is, ar-re we goin' to have coal enough in th' hod whin

th' cold snap comes; will th' plumbin' hold out, an'
will th' job last.

"But they'se wan question that Congress is goin' to take up that you an' me are intherested in.
As a pilgrim father that missed th' first boats, I
must raise me claryon voice again' th' invasion iv this
fair land be th' paupers an' arnychists iv effete Europe. Ye bet I must—because I'm here first. 'Twas
diff'rent whin I was dashed high on th'. stern an'
rockbound coast. In thim days America was th'
refuge iv th' oppressed iv all th' wurruld. They
cud come over here an' do a good job iv oppressin'
thimsilves. As I told ye I come a little late. Th'
Rosenfelts an' th' Lodges bate me be at laste a boat
lenth, an' be th' time I got here they was stern an'
rockbound thimsilves. So I got a gloryous rayciption as soon as I was towed off th' rocks. Th' stars
an' sthripes whispered a welcome in th' breeze an' a
shovel was thrust into me hand an' I was pushed
into a sthreet excyvatin' as though I'd been born here.
Th' pilgrim father who bossed th' job was a fine ol'
puritan be th' name iv Doherty, who come over in
th' Mayflower about th' time iv th' potato rot in
Wexford, an' he made me think they was a hole in
th' breakwather iv th' haven iv refuge an' some iv
th' wash iv th' seas iv oppression had got through.
He was a stern an' rockbound la-ad himsilf, but I was
a good hand at loose stones an' wan day—but I'll
tell ye about that another time.

"Annyhow, I was rayceived with open arms that
sometimes ended in a clinch. I was afraid I wasn't

goin' to assimilate with th' airlyer pilgrim fathers
an' th' instichoochions iv th' counthry, but I soon
found that a long swing iv th' pick made me as good
as another man an' it didn't require a gr-reat intellect,
or sometimes anny at all, to vote th' dimmycrat ticket,
an' befure I was here a month, I felt enough like a
native born American to burn a witch. Wanst in a
while a mob iv intilligint collajeens, whose grand-
fathers had bate me to th' dock, wud take a shy at me
Pathrick's Day procission or burn down wan iv me
churches, but they got tired iv that befure long; 'twas
too much like wurruk.

"But as I tell ye, Hinnissy, 'tis diff'rent now. I
don't know why 'tis diff'rent but 'tis diff'rent. 'Tis
time we put our back again' th' open dure an' keep
out th' savage horde. If that cousin iv ye'ers ex-
pects to cross, he'd betther tear f'r th' ship. In
a few minyits th' gates 'll be down an' whin th' oppressed wurruld comes hikin' acrost to th' haven iv
refuge, they'll do well to put a couplin' pin undher
their hats, f'r th' Goddess iv Liberty 'll meet thim
at th' dock with an axe in her hand. Congress is goin' to fix it. Me frind Shaughnessy says so. He was
in yisterdah an' says he: ' 'Tis time we done something to make th' immigration laws sthronger,' says
he. 'Thrue f'r ye, Miles Standish,' says I; 'but
what wud ye do?' 'I'd keep out th' offscourin's iv
Europe,' says he. 'Wud ye go back?' says I.
'Have ye'er joke,' says he. ' 'Tis not so seeryus
as it was befure ye come,' says I. 'But what ar-re
th' immygrants doin' that's roonous to us?' I says.

'Well,' says he, 'they're arnychists,' he says; 'they don't assymilate with th' counthry,' he says. 'Maybe th' counthry's digestion has gone wrong fr'm too much rich food,' says I; 'perhaps now if we'd lave off thryin' to digest Rockyfellar an' thry a simple diet like Schwartzmeister, we wudden't feel th' effects iv our vittels,' I says. 'Maybe if we'd season th' immygrants a little or cook thim thurly, they'd go down betther,' I says.

" 'They 're arnychists, like Parsons,' he says. 'He wud've been an immygrant if Texas hadn't been admitted to th' Union,' I says. 'Or Snolgosh,' he says. 'Has Mitchigan seceded?' I says. 'Or Gittoo,' he says. 'Who come fr'm th' effete monarchies iv Chicago, west iv Ashland Av'noo,' I says. 'Or what's-his-name, Wilkes Booth,' he says. 'I don't know what he was—maybe a Boolgharyen,' says I. 'Well, annyhow,' says he, 'they're th' scum iv th' earth.' 'They may be that,' says I; 'but we used to think they was th' cream iv civilization,' I says. 'They're off th' top annyhow. I wanst believed 'twas th' best men iv Europe come here, th' la-ads that was too sthrong and indepindant to be kicked around be a boorgomasther at home an' wanted to dig out f'r a place where they cud get a chanst to make their way to th' money. I see their sons fightin' into politics an' their daughters tachin' young American idee how to shoot too high in th' public school, an' I thought they was all right. But I see I was wrong. Thim boys out there towin' wan heavy foot afther th' other to th' rowlin' mills is all arnychists. There's

[ 52 ]

warrants out f'r all names endin' in 'inski, an' I
think I'll board up me windows, f'r,' I says, 'if
immygrants is as dangerous to this counthry as ye an'
I an' other pilgrim fathers believe they are, they'se
enough iv thim sneaked in already to make us abor-
igines about as infloointial as the prohibition vote in
th' Twinty-ninth Ward. They'll dash again' our
stern an' rock-bound coast till they bust it,' says I.

" ' But I ain't so much afraid as ye ar-re. I'm not
afraid iv me father an' I'm not afraid iv mesilf. An'
I'm not afraid iv Schwartzmeister's father or Hinnery
Cabin Lodge's grandfather. We all come over th'
same way, an' if me ancestors were not what Hogan
calls rigicides, 'twas not because they were not ready
an' willin', on'y a king niver come their way. I don't
believe in killin' kings, mesilf. I niver wud've
sawed th' block off that curly-headed potintate that
I see in th' pitchers down town, but, be hivins, Presarved Codfish Shaughnessy, if we'd begun a few
years ago shuttin' out folks that wudden't mind
handin' a bomb to a king, they wudden't be enough
people in Mattsachoosetts to make a quorum f'r th'
Anti-Impeeryal S'ciety,' says I. ' But what wud ye
do with th' offscourin' iv Europe? ' says he. ' I'd
scour thim some more,' says I.

" An' so th' meetin' iv th' Plymouth Rock Assocyation come to an end. But if ye wud like to get
it together, Deacon Hinnissy, to discuss th' immy-
gration question, I'll sind out a hurry call f'r
Schwartzmeister an' Mulcahey an' Ignacio Sbarbaro
an' Nels Larsen an' Petrus Gooldvink, an' we 'll

[ 53 ]

gather to-night at Fanneilnoviski Hall at th' corner
iv Sheridan an' Sigel sthreets. All th' pilgrim fathers
is rayquested f'r to bring interpreters."

" Well," said Mr. Hennessy, " divvle th' bit I care,
on'y I'm here first, an' I ought to have th' right to
keep th' bus fr'm bein' overcrowded."

" Well," said Mr. Dooley, " as a pilgrim father
on me gran' nephew's side, I don't know but ye're
right. An' they'se wan sure way to keep thim out."

" What's that? " asked Mr. Hennessy.

" Teach thim all about our instichoochions befure
they come," said Mr. Dooley.

# White House Discipline

"WHERE did ye spind th' New Year's?" asked Mr. Dooley. "I didn't go to th' White House rayciption," said Mr. Hennessy, pleasantly.

"I see ye didn't," said Mr. Dooley. "Ye'er ar-rm is not in a sling. Man an' boy, Hinnissy, I've taken manny a chanst on me life, but I'd as lave think iv declarin' th' sintimints iv me heart in an Orange meetin' as dhroppin' in f'r a socyal call at what Hogan calls th' ixicutive mansion. That is, if I was a govermint emplyee, which I ain't, havin' been born wrong.

"Th' time was whin a man lost his job an' his heart to th' prisidint at th' same time. A reproof was administhered to him with chloryform. He woke up an' rubbed his eyes an' says, 'Where am I?' an' th' polisman says: 'Ye're in an ash bar'l.' He come fr'm th' White House with tears in his eyes an' was tol' he was out iv wurruk. But, Hinnissy, th' prisint occypant iv th' White House is a heartier person. A reproof fr'm him is th' same thing as a compound fracture. A wurrud iv caution will lay a man up f'r a week an' a severe riprimand will sind him through life with a wooden leg.

"There was me frind, Gin'ral Miles. No more gallant sojer iver dhrew his soord to cut out a

patthern f'r a coat thin Gin'ral Miles. He's hunted th'
Apachy, th' Sioux, th' Arapahoo, th' Comanchee, th'
Congressman an' other savages iv th' plain; he's faced
death an' promotion in ivry form, an' no harm come
to him till he wint up th' White House stairs or maybe
'twas till he come down. Annyhow, Gin'ral Miles was
pursooin' th' thrue coorse iv a nachral warryor an'
enlightenin' th' wurruld on th' things he happened
to think iv. 'Tis what is ixpicted iv him. If ye don't
read him ye don't know what's goin' on in th' wurruld.
Ivry Sundah I pick up me pa-aper an' hurry through
th' articles on what's a suitable Christmas gift f'r th'
hired girl who'll pizen th' soup if she gets three yards
iv calico, be Winnyfield Scott Schley, an' what ought
to be done f'r th' Chinee, be Cap. Mahan, an' get
down to what Gin'ral Miles thinks. 'Tis always good
an' full iv meaty advice. ' Is Mars inhabited? '
' Th' future iv th' Columbya river salmon,' ' Is white
lead good f'r th' complexion? ' ' What wud I do
if I had a millyion dollars an' it was so,' ' England's
supreemacy in Cochin China,' ' Pink gaiters as a
necissity iv warfare,' ' Is th' Impire shouldhers goin'
out? ' ' Waist measurements iv warriors I have met,'
an' so on. Gin'ral Miles is th' on'y in-an'-out, up
an' down, catch-as-catch-can, white, red or black,
with or without, journylist we have left. On anny
subject fr'm stove polish to sun worship, I'd take th'
wurrud iv me frind Gin'ral Miles befure th' man that
made th' goods.

" 'Twas that got him into throuble. Wan day
afther inspictin' th' army, Gin'ral Miles give a chat

to wan iv his fav'rite journals on what he thought
about th' navy, him bein' a great authority on navy
affairs befure steam come in.  I don't know what
th' divvle he said an' I don't care, f'r me mind was
made up long ago, an' ivrybody that don't agree
with me is little betther thin a thraitor or a cow'rd.
But annyhow he give his opinyion, an' afther givin'
it he took his bonnet out, had a goold beater in to
fix up th' epylets, got th' ilicthric lights goin' in th'
buttons, found th' right pair iv blue an' pink pants,
pulled on th' shoes with th' silver bells, harnessed to
his manly hips th' soord with the forget-me-nots on
th' handle an' pranced over to th' White House.  As
he wint up th' hall, he noticed an atmosphere iv what
Hogan calls cold hatoor, f'r wan iv th' durekeepers
said th' prisidint wasn't home an' another lightly
kicked him as he passed, but like a sojer he wint on
to th' East room where Mr. Rosenfelt, th' pa-apers
tells me, shtud in front iv th' fireplace, nervously
pluckin' Sicrety Gage be th' beard.  ' I've come,'
says Gin'ral Miles, ' to pay me rayspicts to th' head
iv th' naytion.'  ' Thank ye,' says th' prisidint, ' I'll
do th' same f'r th' head iv th' army,' he says, bounc-
in' a coal scuttle on th' vethran's helmet.  ' Gin'ral,
I don't like ye'er recent conduct,' he says, sindin' th'
right to th' pint iv th' jaw.  ' Ye've been in th' army
forty year,' he says, pushin' his head into th' grate,
' an' ye shud know that an officer who criticizes his
fellow officers, save in th' reg'lar way, that is to say
in a round robin, is guilty iv I dinnaw what,' he
says, feedin' him with his soord.  ' I am foorced to

administher ye a severe reproof,' he says. ' Is that
what this is?' says Gin'ral Miles. '.It is,' says th'
prisidint. ' I thought it was capital punishmint,'
says Gin'ral Miles as he wint out through th' window
pursooed be a chandelier. His nex' article will be entitled ' Hospital Sketches,' an' I undhershtand he's
dictatin' a few remarks to his nurse on providin' atthractive suits iv steel plate f'r gin'rals in th' army.

" Well, sir, they'll be gr-reat times down there f'r
a few years. A movement is on foot f'r to establish
an emergency hospital f'r office holders an' politicians
acrost th' sthreet fr'm th' White House where they
can be threated f'r infractions iv th' Civil Sarvice
law followed be pers'nal injuries. I'll be watchin'
th' pa-apers ivry mornin'. ' Rayciption at th' White
House. Among th' casulties was so-an'-so. Th'
prisidint was in a happy mood. He administhered a
stingin' rebuke to th' Chief Justice iv th' Supreme
Coort, a left hook to eye. Sinitor Hanna was prisint walkin' with a stick. Th' prisidint approached
him gaily an' asked him about his leg. " 'Tis
gettin' betther," says th' sinitor. " That's good,"
says th' prisidint. " Come again whin it is entirely
well an' we'll talk over that appointment," he says.
Th' afthernoon was enlivened be th' appearance iv
a Southern Congressman askin' f'r a foorth-class
post-office. Th' prisidint hardly missed him be more
thin a foot at th' gate, but th' Congressman bein'
formerly wan iv Mosby's guerillas escaped, to th'
gr-reat chagrin iv Mr. Rosenfelt, who remarked on
his return that life at th' White House was very

confinin'. " I will niver be able to enfoorce th' civil
sarvice law till I take more exercise," he said heartily.
Th' ambulance was at th' dure promptly at five, but
no important business havin' been thransacted nearly
all th' cabinet was able to walk to their homes.'

" Yes, sir, 'twill be grand an' I'm goin' to injye it.
F'r th' first time since I've been at it, Ar-rchey road
methods has been inthrajooced in naytional polliticks.
I knew th' time wud come, Hinnissy. 'Tis th' on'y
way. Ye may talk about it as much as ye want, but
govermint, me boy, is a case iv me makin' ye do what
I want an' if I can't do it with a song, I'll do it with
a shovel. Th' ir'n hand in th' velvet glove, th' horseshoe in th' boxin' mit, th' quick right, an' th' heavy
boot, that was th' way we r-run polliticks when I was
captain iv me precinct."

" But ye niver was prisidint," said Mr. Hennessy.

" I always had too soft a spot f'r age," said Mr.
Dooley; " an' 'tis th' aged that does up us young
fellows. An' annyhow I done betther."

# Money and Matrimony

"CAN a man marry on twinty-five dollars?" asked Mr. Dooley.

"He can if he can get th' money," said Mr. Hennessy.

"Well, sir," said Mr. Dooley; "here's a judge on th' binch says twinty-five dollars is as much as a man needs to enther th' sacred bonds—twinty-five dollars beside th' nerve, an' he has to have that annyhow. Th' pa-apers has took it up an' some is f'r it an' some is again' it. A few iditors believes it can be done on less; others thinks it can't be done undher thirty at th' outside. A larned lawyer says that a man who wud lure a young girl away fr'm her music lessons whin if she asked him f'r twinty-six dollars he'd have to signal f'r help, is nawthin' short iv a crim'nal. Nearly all th' ladin' acthresses in th' counthry has been interviewed an' they say that if marrid at all they cud not see their way clear f'r less thin a millyion iv money. They think th' judge meant a divoorce. Lookin' over th' argymints pro an' con, Hinnissy, I come to th' conclusion that th' judge is wrong an' times has changed.

"Whin I was a boy all a man needed was a little encouragement fr'm th' fam'ly, an account with a liveryman an' a small pull with th' parish priest an' there he was. 'Twas well if he had a job too but if he hadn't it wasn't a bar. A marrid man can always find wurruk to do. He's got to. But no wan iver thought iv askin' him to skin open his bank book. They wasn't anny such things. They wasn't anny banks. He didn't have to pin a cashier's check to th' proposal an' put in a sealed bid. If th' girls in my time an' this part iv town had to wait f'r an opulent business man with twenty-five or thirty dollars, manny iv thim wud be waitin' at this minyit.

"We looked on mathrimony as a dhraft on posterity, as Mark Hanna wud say, an' not as an invistmint. We argyied that while th' childher was growin' up we'd be undher no expinse, an' when they'd finished their schoolin' an' was able to take up th' stern jooties iv life an' go to wurruk, say between th' age iv sivin an' nine, they cud support us in luxury. Th' young ladies had none th' best iv us. They had no money too, along with th' rest iv their charms. It was no case iv matchin' coopons in thim happy days. Th' father iv th' fam'ly niver thought iv sindin' in an expert accountant to look over th' young man's books an' decide whether his invistmints was sound, an' if th' young man had th' nerve to ask his father-in-law was he still on th' payroll, 'twudn't be the sacramint iv mathrimony he'd require. If th' young man was kind to th' dog, smoked seegars that were not made be th' rubber thrust an' cud pass ivry second saloon without a pang, he was illegible f'r to enther th' first fam'lies in th' neighborhood an' sometimes even th' last. We was too dilicate f'r to speak iv marredge as though it was like buyin' a

pound iv tinpinny nails. Durin' th' coortship no wan
around th' house iver let on that annything was in
th' air, though wanst in awhile they was a giggle whin
th' dure bell rang an' th' ol' man wud give a wink to
th' clock an' go out into th' kitchen. We spint most
iv our time in th' kitchen while th' preliminaries was
bein' arranged. Th' coortship I think wint on be a
complete system iv signals long befure Marconi come
into th' wurruld, but wan night th' wealthy heiress
come back fr'm th' parlor an' fell into a clinch with
her mother, an' th' proud father yawned an' wint to
bed. That was all they was to it. No wan assayed
young Lotharyo Hinnissy iv th' sixth ward. If they
heard he had twinty-five dollars, they'd begin f'r to
make an allybi ready f'r him. I mind whin Hogan
was goin' to marry Cassidy's daughter. ' I haven't
a cint,' he says. ' Hurry up an' marry thin,' says
Cassidy, ' or ye might have.'

" That's th' way it was in thim good ol' days an',
be hivins, I think that's th' way it is now among th'
likes iv us. An' that's a good thing f'r th' men that
own th' rollin' mills. It wudden't do to take anny
chances goin' up an' down Ar-rchey road offerin'
ye'ersilf without th' cash forfeit. Some wan might
call ye. But it's diff'rent among th' best fam'lies.
'Tis far diff'rent. I read be th' pa-apers in this con-
throvarsy that if a man can't show down a bank
account that wud make Andhrew Carnaygie feel like
goin' back to wurruk, he might as well make up his
mind to remain a gay bachelor till he falls fr'm th'
cab f'r th' las' time. Not f'r him th' joys iv marrid

life, th' futman at th' dure tellin' him his wife has not
come home yet, th' prattlin' iv th' tendher infant as it
is rocked to sleep in th' incybator, th' frequent letthers fr'm abroad askin' him if th' dhraft come. No
rayspictible.woman wud have him while he was gettin'
th' money an' none ought to have him afther he's
got it.

"Manetime th' price iv mathrimonyal coopon fours
goes up till hardly annywan can think iv entherin'
thim. A man believes th' judge was wrong an' says
he, ' I'll niver condimn Mary Josephine to be a poor
man's wife. I'll wait till I get a millyion.' It's not
so hard to get a millyion nowadays if ye pick out
th' right people to get it fr'm, but it takes some time,
an' befure th' eager suitor has landed enough to sit
in th' game, he's considherably past th' age iv consint.
Manetime father, too, hasn't been idle. He's be-
thrayed a few thrusts himsilf an' put a story or two
on th' house. So whin th' young man comes up wan
night an' lays down his pile an' suggests that th'
time has come f'r to hasten th' glad evint, father
says: ' I'm afraid, me boy, that ye're a little slow.
Ye haven't kept pace with th' socyal requiremints.
Since seein' ye last, Mary Josephine has acquired th'
use iv a private yacht an' is slowly mastherin' th'
great truth that if ye have a club suit, ye ought to
pass up th' make. A slight oversight some afthernoon in distinguishin' thrumps an' they wudden't be
enough iv that bundle left to put a rubber band
around. No, Mike, I think a gr-reat deal iv ye, but
niver, niver will I consint that a daughter iv mine shud

suffer th' pangs iv poverty.' An' so it goes through th' years until marredge, Hinnissy, is resthricted to th' very rich an' th' exthremely poor who're almost all marrid already.

" I don't know mesilf what to think iv it, Hinnissy, an' I don't know that I ought to worry about it. I haven't noticed anny reduction in th' number iv marredge licenses day be day. Th' Kubelowskis an' th' Witsinskis still are exchangin' vows, an' if they've got more thin twenty-five dollars apiece I'd like to know where they got it an' notify th' polis. No, sir, th' gloryous ol' instichooshion iv which I'm as proud as I am shy is here to stay, an' I'm thinkin' it'll be here whin money becomes extinct. If th' rich are becomin' richer, th' poor are becomin' more foolish about these things, an' there's hope in that."

" D'ye ra-ally think a man ought to marry on twenty-five dollars? " asked Mr. Hennessy.

" If he's that kind iv a man, more money thin that wud be wasted on him," said Mr. Dooley.

# Prince Henry's Visit

"IT'S goin' to be gr-reat times f'r us Germans whin Prince Hinnery comes over," said Mr. Dooley.

"By th' way," said Mr. Hennessy with an air of polite curiosity, "what relation's he to th' impror iv Germany? Is he th' son or th' nevvew?"

"He's nayther," said Mr. Dooley. "Th' impror has no sons that I iver heerd iv. If he had a son he'd be a steam injine. No, sir, this man is th' impror's brother Hinnery or Hans. I don't exactly know what th' usual jooties iv an impror's brother is. I know what an impror has to do. His wurruk's cut out f'r him. I cud fill th' job mesilf to me own satisfaction an' th' on'y wan an impror has to plaze is himsilf. Th' German impror frequently mintions another, but on'y in th' way iv politeness. I know what an impror's jooties is, but I don't know what an impror's brother has to do ex officio, as Hogan says. But this boy Hinnery or Hans has more wurruk thin a bartinder in a prohibition town. He's a kind iv travellin' agent f'r th' big la-ad. His bag is ready packed ivry night, he sleeps like a fireman with his pants in his boots beside his bed, an' they'se a thrap dure alongside th' cradle f'r him to slide down to th' first flure.

"He's no more thin got to sleep whin th' three

iliven sounds on th' gong. In Hinnery leaps to th'
pantaloons, down th' laddher he goes pullin' up
his suspinders with wan hand an' puttin' on his hat
with th' other an' off he is f'r Corea or Chiny or Booloochistan at a gallop. His brother stands at th' dure
an' hollers farewell to him. ' Go, Hinnery,' he says.
' Go, me dear brother, to th' land iv perpetchooal
sunshine an' knock in nails f'r to hang up th' German
armor,' he says. ' Knock in th' nails, an' if ye happen
to hit ye'ersilf on th' thumb, swear on'y be th' German Mike an' raymimber ye done it f'r me,' he says.
' I will remain at home an'' conthrol th' rest iv th'
wurruld with th' assistance iv that German Prov-
idence that has been as kind to us as we desarve an'
that we look up to as our akel,' he says. An' Hinnery
goes away. He travels o'er land an' sea, be fire an'
flood an' field. He's th' ginooine flyin' Dutchman.
His home is in his hat. He hasn't slept all night in
a bed f'r tin years. 'Tis Hinnery this an' Hinnery
that; Hinnery up th' Nile an' Hinnery to Injy; Hinnery here an' Hinnery there. Th' cuffs iv his shirt
is made iv th' time cards iv railroads. Ivry time
they'se a change in schedool he ordhers new shirts.
He knows th' right iv way fr'm Berlin to Ballyma-
choo; he speaks all known languages, an' ivrywhere
he goes he makes a frind or an inimy, which is th'
same thing to th' Germans. He carries a sample
case undher wan arm an' a gun undher th' other, an'
if ye don't like Rhine wine perhaps ye'll take lead.
On second considherations he won't shoot ye but he'll
sell ye th' Krupp. They'se more where it come fr'm.

[ 74 ]

## Prince Henry's Visit

"I tell ye, Hinnissy, this Impror or Kaiser iv Germany is a smart man. I used to think 'twas not so. I thought he had things unaisy in his wheel-house. I mind whin he got th' job, ivrywan says: 'Look out f'r war. This wild man will be in that office f'r a year whin he'll just about declare fight with th' wurruld.' An' ivrybody framed up f'r him. But look ye what happened. 'Tis twinty years since he was swore in an' ne'er a fight has he had. Ivrybody else has been in throuble. A screw-maker iv a sindintary life has ploonged England into a war; me frinds th' Greeks that were considhered about akel to a flush iv anger over a raid on a push cart has mixed it up with th' Turks; th' Japs has been at war, an' th' Dagoes; our own peace-lovin' nation has been runnin' wan short an' wan serryal war, an' aven th' Chinese has got their dandher up, be hivins, but Willum, th' Middleweight Champeen, Willum th' Potsdam Game Chicken, Willum, th' Unterdenlinden Cyclone, Willum has been ladin' th' ca'm an' prosperous life iv a delicatessen dealer undher a turner hall. He's had no fights. He niver will have anny fights. He 'll go to his grave with th' repytation iv nayether winnin' nor losin' a battle, but iv takin' down more forfeits thin anny impror pugilist iv our time.

"What do I think iv him? Well, sir, I think he's not a fighter but a fight lover. Did ye iver see wan iv thim young men that always has a front seat at a scrap so near th' ring that whin th' second blows th' wather he gets what's left on his shirt front? Well, that's me frind Willum. He is a pathron iv

[ 75 ]

spoort an' not a spoort. His ideel is war but he's a practical man. He has a season ticket to th' matches but he niver will put on the gloves. He's in the spoortin' goods business an' he usu'lly gets a per-cintage iv th' gate receipts. If he sees two nations bellowin' at each other th' assurances iv their dis-tinguished considheration, he says: ' Boys, get to-gether. 'Tis a good match. Ye're both afraid. Go in, uncle; go in, Boer.' He is all around th' ring-side, encouragin' both sides. ' Stand up again' him there, Paul; rassle him to th' flure. Good f'r ye, uncle. A thrifle low, that wan, but all's fair in war. Defind ye'er indipindance, noble sons iv Teutonic blood. Exercise ye'er sov'reign rights, me English frinds.' If wan or th' other begins to weaken th' first bottle through th' ropes is Willum's. Whin anny-body suggests a dhraw, he demands his money back. Nawthin' but a fight to a finish will do him. If ayether iv th' contestants is alive in th' ring at th' end, he congratulates him an' asks him if he heerd that German cheer in th' las' round.

" Oh, he's good. He'll do all right, that German man. In high di-plomacy, he's what in low di-plom-acy wud be called a happy jollyer. But he knows that if a man's always slappin' ye on th' back, ye begin to think he's weak; so he first shakes his fist undher ye'er nose an' thin slaps ye on th' back. Some-times he does both at th' same time. An' he's got th' thrue jollyer's way iv provin' to ye that he's ye'er frind alone an' th' deadly inimy iv all others. He's got th' Czar iv Rooshya hypnotized, th' King iv

England hugged to a standstill, an' th' Impror iv
Chiny in tears. An' he's made thim all think th'
first thing annywan knows, he'll haul off an' swing
on wan iv th' others.

" So, havin' fixed ivrything up in Europe, he cast
his eyes on this counthry, an' says he: ' I think I'll
have to dazzle thim furriners somewhat. They've
got a round-headed man f'r prisidint that was born
with spurs on his feet an' had a catridge-belt f'r a
rattle, an' some day his goolash won't agree with
him an' he'll call th' bluff I've been makin' these
manny years. What'll I do to make thim me frinds
so that 'twud be like settin' fire to their own house
to attackt me? Be hivins, I've got it. They're a
dimmycratic people. I'll sind thim a prince. They
can't keep him away, an' whin he lands, th' German
popylation'll come out an' get up schootzenfists f'r him
an' me fellow impror acrost th' say'll see how manny
iv them there ar-re, an' he'll think twict befure he
makes faces at me. F'r, wanst a German, always a
German be it iver so far,' he says. ' I'll sind thim
Hinnery. Hinnery! Turn in th' alarm f'r Hinnery,' he says. Hinnery slides down th' pole an'
th' Impror says: ' Brother, catch th' night boat f'r
America an' pay a visit to whativer king they have
there. Take along annywan ye like an' as manny
thrunks as ye need, an' stay as long as ye plaze.
Don't ring. Back th' dhray again' th' front dure
an' hurl ye'ersilf into th' first bed room ye see. Act
just as if ye was me,' he says. ' But I'm not invited,'
says Hinnery. ' Write ye'er own invitation,' says

Willum. ' Here's th' answer: ' Fellow Potyntate, Ye'ers iv th' second instant askin' me brother Hinnery to spind a year with ye, not received. In reply will say that nawthin' cud give me gr-reater pleasure. He can stay as long as he plazes. Him an' his soot will not need more thin th' whole house, so ye can have th' barn to ye'ersilf. If ye have a brother, don't neglect to sind him over to see me. I know a good hotel at four a day, all included but candles, an' if he stands at th' front window, he can see me go by anny day. Ye'ers, Willum, Rex an' a shade more.'

" So here comes Hinnery, an' we're goin' to give him a gloryous rayciption. Th' war vessels will be out to welcome him, th' prisidint will meet him at th' dock an' he will be threated to wan continyous round iv schutzenfists, turnd'yeminds, sangerbunds, katzenjammers, skats, an' other German fistivals. Th' aristocracy iv New York is practicin' Dutch an' th' Waldorf-Astorya will be festooned with dachshunds. He'll see more Germans an' more German Germans thin he iver see in Prooshya. An' I hope he'll have a good time."

" I wondher what Tiddy Rosenfelt thinks iv it? " asked Mr. Hennessy.

" Well, what wud ye think if ye'd had to intertain a German Prince unawares? Ye'd give him th' best ye'd got, ye'd dig up a bottle iv Knockimheimer down th' sthreet an' ye'd see that he got a noodle ivry time he reached. An' whin he wint away, ye'd go as far as th' dure with him an' pat him on th' back an' say: ' Good-bye, good-bye, Hinnery. Good-bye, Hans.

[ 78 ]

Guten nobben, oof veedersayin, me boy. Good luck
to ye. Look out f'r that shtep! There ye ar-re. Be
careful iv th' gate. D'ye think ye can get home
all right? I'd go as far as th' car with ye if I had
me coat on. Well, good-bye lanksman. Raymimber
me to ye'er brother. Tell him not to f'rget that little
matther. Oh, of coorse, they'se no counthry in th'
wurruld like Germany an' we're uncivilized an'
rapacyous an' will get our heads knocked off if we
go into a fight. Good-bye, mein frind.' An' whin
ye'd shut th' dure on him, ye'd say: ' Well, what d'ye
think iv that? ' "

# Prince Henry's Reception

"THAT Prince Hinnery seems to be havin' a good time," said Mr. Hennessy.

"He's havin' th' time iv his life," said Mr. Dooley. "Not since th' Hohnezollern fam'ly was founded be wan iv th' ablest burglars iv th' middle ages has anny prince injyed such a spree as this wan. Ye see, a prince is a gr-reat man in th' ol' counthry, but he niver is as gr-reat over there as he is here. Whin he's at home he's something th' people can't help an' they don't mind him. He's like an iron lamp post, station'ry, ornymintal, an' useful to let people know where they are. But whin he comes to this home iv raypublican simplicity, he's all that th' wurrud prince wud imply, an' it implies more to us thin to annywan else. I tell ye, we're givin' him th' best we have in th' shop. We're showin' him that whativer riv'rince we may feel tow'rd George Wash'nton, it don't prejudice us again' live princes. Th' princes we hate is thim that are dead an' harmless. We've rayceived him with open arms, an' I'll say this f'r him, that f'r a German he's a good fellow.

"That's as far as I care to go, havin' lived f'r manny years among th' Germans. I'm not prejudiced again' thim, mind ye. They make good beer an' good citizens an' mod-rate polismen, an' they are fond iv their fam'lies an' cheese. But wanst a

German, always Dutch. Ye cudden't make Americans iv thim if ye called thim all Perkins an' brought thim up in Worcester. A German niver ra-aly leaves Germany. He takes it with him wheriver he goes. Whin an Irishman is four miles out at sea he is as much an American as Presarved Fish. But a German is niver an American excipt whin he goes back to Germany to see his rilitives. He keeps his own language, he plays pinochle, he despises th' dhrink iv th' counthry, his food is sthrange an' he on'y votes f'r Germans f'r office, or if he can't get a German, f'r somewan who's again' th' Irish. I bet ye, if ye was to suddenly ask Schwarzmeister where he is, he'd say: 'At Hockheimer in Schwabia.' He don't ra-aly know he iver come to this counthry. I've heerd him talkin' to himsilf. He always counts in German.

"But I say about Prince Hinnery that f'r a German he's all right an' I'm glad he come. I hear he wrote home to his brother that is th' Imp'ror over there: 'Dear Willum: This is a wondherful counthry, an' they've give me a perfectly killin' rayciption. I've almost died laughin'. We was met forty miles out at sea be a band on a raft playin' th' Watch on th' Rhine. We encountered another band playin' th' same plazin' harmony ivry five miles till we got up to New York. I wisht I had come over on a man-iv-war. In th' Bay we was surrounded be a fleet iv tugs carryin' riprisintatives iv th' press, singin' th' Watch on th' Rhine. I rayceived siveral offers through a migaphone to write an article about what ye say in ye'er sleep f'r th' pa-apers, but I declined thim, awaitin' insthructions fr'm ye. At th' dock we was greeted be a band playin' th' Watch on th' Rhine an' afther some delay, caused be th' Delicatessen Sangerbund holdin' us while they sung th' Watch on th' Rhine, we stepped ashore on a gangplank neatly formed be th' guv'nor iv th' state holdin' onto th' feet iv th' mayor, him clutchin' th' iditor iv th' Staats Zeitung an' so on, th' gangplank singin' th' Watch on th' Rhine as we walked to th' dock.

" ' I am much imprissed be New York. I hate it. Th' buildin's are very high here but th' language is higher. If I was to go home now, ye wudden't know me. Afther I hear a speech I don't dare to look in th' glass f'r fear I might be guilty iv treason to ye, mein lieber. Our illustrious ancesthor, Fridrick th' Great, was a cheap an' common man compared to me, an' ye, august brother, niver got by th' barrier. I hope I'll have time to cool down befure I get home or ye'll have to lock me up.

" ' They're givin' me th' fine line iv entertainmint. Ivrywhere I go, they'se music or something that does as well. I have a musical insthrument called a catastrophone in me room that plays th' Watch on th' Rhine whin I go in at night an' get up in th' mornin'. Whin I go out on th' sthreet, th' crowd cries " Hock th' Kaiser." I wish they'd stop hockin' ye, dear brother, an' hock th' Watch on th' Rhine. (This here is an American joke. I'm gettin' on fast.) I'm goin' to be took to th' opry some night this week. They've fired a lot iv la-ads out iv their boxes to make

room f'r me. Wan iv thim objected, but he was fired
annyhow. Aftherward I'm goin' to ate dinner with
th' iditors iv th' counthry. Won't that be nice? I
suppose I'm th' first Hohnezollern that iver took dinner with an iditor, though our fam'ly has often given
thim food an' lodgin'—in jail. I wish ye was here
to go with me. Ye've had more journylistic expeeryence an' manny iv th' things ye've had printed wudden't seem too unthrue to th' other guests. Th' newspapers has been mos' kind to me, I might say almost
too kind. I am sindin' ye a photygraft iv mesilf in
me bath, took be flashlight be an iditor concealed on
th' top iv th' clothes press, an' an interview be a lady
rayporther who riprisinted hersilf as th' Queen iv
Ohio.

" ' But th' big ivint comes off tomorrah. I am
actually invited to a dinner iv wan hundherd iv th'
riprisintative business men iv New York an' a few
Christyans ast in aftherward. Hooray, hooray!
Mind ye, these ar-re not ordhn'ry business men. Far
fr'm it. No one gets in unless he has made at laste
eight millyion marks out iv th' sivinty millyion marks
in this counthry. An' I'm ast to meet thim! What
fun! I bet 'twill be jolly. I'm goin' to buy me a
table f'r computin' inthrest, a copy iv th' naytional
bankin' act an' a good account iv th' thransactions
in sterlin' exchange f'r th' current year an' whin th'
quip an' jest go round, I'll be no skeleton at th' feast.

" ' Ye can see be this that me life has been almost
too gay, but th' merrymint goes blithely on. Fr'm
here I go to Bawstown where I expict to pat th'

[ 86 ]

Bunker Hill monymint on th' head an' have a look
at th' new railway station. Then I will take in
Buffly, Cichago (pro-nounced Sichawgo), Saint
Looey, Three Rapids, Idaho, Pinnsylvanya, an' mos'
iv th' large cities iv th' west, includin' Chatahooga
where wan iv th' gr-reat battles iv th' rivolution was
fought between Gin'ral Sigel an' Gin'ral Zollycoffer.
I ixpict to larn a good deal about th' steel, pork, corn,
lard an' lithrachoor iv th' counthry befure I rayturn.
But this buttherfly existence is killin' me. It is far
too gay. I suppose whin I was younger, I wud've
injyed it, but me time f'r socyal fistivities has passed
an' I long f'r th' quiet iv home life among th' simple
ryelties iv Europe. Ye'ers, Hinnery.'

"Yes, he's havin' a good time. But what th'
pa-apers calls th' climax iv th' intertainmint will be
reached whin he arrives in Chicago. Schwartzmeister
an' I will rayceive him. Schwartzmeister's fam'ly
knew his in th' ol' counthry. He had an uncle that
was booted all th' way fr'm Sedan to Paris be a cousin
iv th' Prince. We've arranged th' programme as far
as Ar-rchey road is consarned. Monday mornin',
visit to Kennedy's packin' house; afthernoon, Rior-
dan's blacksmith shop; avenin', ' Th' Two Orphans,'
at th' Halsted sthreet opry house. Choosdah, iliven
A.M., inspiction iv th' rollin' mills; afthernoon, visit
to Feeney's coal yard; avenin', ' Bells iv Corneville,'
at th' opry house. Winsdah mornin', tug ride on th'
river fr'm Thirty-first sthreet to Law's coal yard;
afthernoon, a call on th' tanneries, th' cable barn an'
th' brick yards; avenin', dinner an' rayciption be

[ 87 ]

th' retail saloonkeepers. There's th' whole programme. They may think in New York they are
givin' him a good time but we'll show him what gayety
ra-aly is, an' inform him iv th' foundation iv our
supreemacy as a nation. That's what he wants to
see an' we'll show it to him."

" Goowan," said Mr. Hennessy. " He don't know
ye."

" I bet ye he knows me as much as he knows thim,"
said Mr. Dooley. " To a ra-ale prince, they can't
be much diff'rence between a man who sells liquor be
th' pail an' wan that sells it be th' distillery, between
a man that makes a horseshoe an' wan that makes a
millyion tons iv steel. We're all alike to him—Carnaygie, Rockyfellar, Morgan, Schwartzmeister an'
me."

" Well, he certainly has been well rayceived," said
Mr. Hennessy.

" I wondher," said Mr. Dooley, " if he thinks 'tis
on th' square! "

# Cuba vs. Beet Sugar

## CUBA VS. BEET SUGAR

"WHAT'S all this about Cubia an' th' Ph'lippeens?" asked Mr. Hennessy. "What's beet sugar?"

"Th' throuble about Cubia is that she's free; th' throuble about beet sugar is we're not; an' th' throuble about th' Ph'lippeens is th' Ph'lippeen throuble," said Mr. Dooley. "As rega-ards Cubia, she's like a woman that th' whole neighborhood helps to divoorce fr'm a crool husband, but nivertheless a husband, an' a miserable home but a home, an' a small credit at th' grocery but a credit, an' thin whin she goes into th' dhressmakin' business, rayfuse to buy annything fr'm her because she's a divoorced woman. We freed Cubia but we didn't free annything she projooces. It wasn't her fault. We didn't think. We expicted that all we had to do was to go down to Sandago with a kinetoscope an' sthrike th' shackles fr'm th' slave an' she'd be comfortable even if she had no other protiction f'r her poor feet. We f'rgot about th' Beet. Most iv us niver thought about that beautiful but fragile flower excipt biled in conniction with pigs' feet or pickled in its own life juice. We didn't know that upon th' Beet hangs th' fate iv th' nation, th' hope iv th' future, th' permanence iv our instichoochions an' a lot iv other things akelly precious. Th' Beet is th' naytional

[ 91 ]

anthem an', be hivins, it looks as though it might be th' naytional motto befure long.

"Well, Cubia got her freedom or something that wud look like th' same thing if she kept it out iv th' rain, but somehow or another it didn't suit her entirely. A sort iv cravin' come over her that it was hard to tell fr'm th' same feelin' iv vacancy that she knew whin she was opprissed be th' Hated Casteel. Hunger, Hinnissy, is about th' same thing in a raypublic as in a dispotism. They'se not much choice iv unhappiness between a hungry slave an' a hungry freeman. Cubia cudden't cuk or wear freedom. Ye can't make freedom into a stew an' ye can't cut a pair iv pants out iv it. It won't bile, fry, bake or fricassee. Ye can't take two pounds iv fresh creamery freedom, a pound iv north wind, a heapin' taycupfull iv naytional aspirations an' a sprinklin' iv bars fr'm th' naytional air, mix well, cuk over a hot fire an' sarve sthraight fr'm th' shtove; ye can't make a dish out iv that that wud nourish a tired freeman whin he comes home afther a hard day's wurruk lookin' f'r a job. So Cubia comes to us an' says she: 'Ye done well by us,' she says. 'Ye give us freedom,' says she, 'an' more thin enough to go round,' she says, 'an' now if ye plaze we'd like to thrade a little iv it back f'r a few groceries,' she says. 'We will wear wan shackle f'r a ham,' says she, 'an' we'll put on a full raygalia iv ball an' chain an' yoke an' fetters an' come-alongs f'r a square meal,' says she.

"That sounds raisonable enough an' bein' be nature

## Cuba vs. Beet Sugar

a gin'rous people whin we don't think, we're about
to help her disthress with whativer we have cold in
th' panthry whin th' thought iv th' Beet crosses our
minds. What will th' Beet say, th' red, th' juicy,
th' sacchrine Beet, th' Beet iv our Fathers, th' Beet
iv Plymouth Rock, Beet iv th' Pilgrim's Pride, Sweet
Beet iv Liberty, iv thee I sing? If we do annything
f'r Cubia, down goes th' Beet, an' with th' Beet
perishes our instichoochions. Th' constichoochion
follows th' Beet ex propria vigore, as Hogan says.
Th' juice iv th' Beet is th' life blood iv our nation.
Whoiver touches a hair iv yon star spangled Beet,
shoot him on th' spot. A bold Beet industhry a counthry's pride whin wanst desthroyed can niver be sup-
plied. ' Beet sugar an' Liberty Now an' Foriver, wan
an' insiprable '—Dan'l Webster. ' Thank Gawd I—
I also—am a Beet '—th' same. ' Gover'mint iv th'
Beet, by th' Beet an' f'r th' Beet shall not perish fr'm
th' earth,'—Abraham Lincoln. An' so, Hinnissy,
we put th' pie back into th' ice-chest where we keep
our honor an' ginerosity an' lock th' dure an' Cubia
goes home, free an' hopeless. D'ye think so? Well,
I don't. Be hivins, Hinnissy, I think th' time has
come whin we've got to say whether we're a nation iv
Beets. I am no serf, but I'd rather be bent undher
th' dispotism iv a Casteel thin undher th' tyranny iv
a Beet. If I've got to be a slave, I'd rather be wan
to a man, even a Spanish man, thin to a viggytable.
If I'm goin' to be opprissed be a Beet, let it be fr'm
th' inside not fr'm without. I'll choose me masther,
Hinnissy, an' whin I do, 'twill not be that low-lyin',

purple-complected, indygistible viggytable. I may
bend me high head to th' egg-plant, th' potato, th'
cabbage, th' squash, th' punkin, th' sparrow-grass,
th' onion, th' spinach, th' rutabaga turnip, th'
Fr-rench pea or th' parsnip, but 'twill niver be said
iv me that I was subjygated be a Beet. No, sir.
Betther death. I'm goin' to begin a war f'r freedom.
I'm goin' to sthrike th' shackles fr'm a slave an' I'm
him. I'm goin' to organize a rig'mint iv Rough
Riders an' whin I stand on th' top iv San Joon hill
with me soord in me hand an' me gleamin' specs on
me nose, ye can mark th' end iv th' domination iv
th' Beet in th' western wurruld. F'r, Hinnissy, I tell
ye what, if th' things I hear fr'm Wash'nton is thrue,
that other war iv freedom stopped befure it was half
done."

" An' what about th' Ph'lippeens? " asked Mr.
Hennessy.

" They'se nawthin' to say about th' Ph'lippeens,"
said Mr. Dooley, " excipt that th' throuble down there
is all over."

" All over? "

" All over."

# Bad Men from the West

"I SEE," said Mr. Hennessy, "th' Sinit has rayfused f'r to confirm th' nommynation iv a man f'r an office out West because he'd been in jail."

"Pro-fissyonal jealousy," said Mr. Dooley. "Ye see, th' fact iv th' matther is th' Sinit don't know what th' people iv th' Far West want an' th' prisidint does. Th' Sinit thinks th' jooty iv th' counthry to th' land iv th' tarantuly is done if they sind out a man too weak in th' lungs to stay in th' East an' wan that can multiply com-pound fractions in his head. But th' prisidint he knows that what's needed in th' Far West is active, intilligent officers that can shoot through th' pocket. Th' other day it become necess'ry to thrust on th' impeeryal terrytory iv Aryzony a competint person f'r to administher th' laws an' keep th' peace iv said community, an' th' pollyticians in Wash'nton was f'r givin' thim some-wan fr'm Connecticut or Rhode Island with a cough an' a brother in th' legislachure. But th' prisidint says no. 'No,' he says, 'none but th' best,' he says, 'f'r th' domain iv th' settin' sun,' he says. 'I know th' counthry well,' he says, 'an' to cope with th' hardy spirits iv Aryzony 'tis issintial we shud have a man that can plug a coyote fr'm th' hip at fifty paces,' he says. 'How can you dhraw to yon hectic flush

so's to make him good again' th' full hands iv thim
communities where life is wan gay an' tireless round
iv shoot,' he says. ' Ye can't expict him to riprisint
th' majesty iv th' govermint iv Wash'nton an'
Lincoln. He'd be bucked off befure he got his feet
in th' sturrups. No, sir, th' man iv me choice is
Tarantula Jake, th' whirlwind iv Zuma Pass. This
imminint statesman has pocketed more balls thin
anny other disperado west iv Tucson, an' anny docy-
mints iv state enthrusted to his hands is sure to be
delivered to their object,' he says, ' or,' he says, ' th'
heirs iv th' object,' he says.

" ' But,' says th' Sinit, ' he lost an ear in a fight.'

" 'A boyish error,' says th' prisidint. ' Th' man
threw th' knife at him,' he says.

" ' And he kilt a man,' says they.

" ' Ye do him an injustice,' says th' prisidint.
' Kilt a man, says ye! Kilt a man! Such is fame.
Why,' he says, ' he's kilt more men thin th' Sinit
has repytations,' he says. ' Ye might jus' as well say
me frind Sinitor Bivridge wanst made a speech, or
that Shakespere wrote a play, or that it's a fine tooth
I have. If all th' people Jake has kilt was alive
to-day, we'd be passin' congisted disthrict ligislachion
f'r Aryzony. Kilt a man is it? I give ye me wurrud
that ye can hardly find wan home in Aryzony, fr'm
th' proudest doby story-an'-a-half palace iv th' rich
to th' lowly doby wan-story hut iv th' poor, that this
flagrant pathrite hasn't deprived iv at laste wan
ornymint. Didn't I tell ye he is a killer? I didn't
mane a man that on'y wanst in a while takes a life.

## Bad Men from the West

He's a rale killer. He's no retailer. He's th' Armour
iv that particular line iv slaughter. Ye don't suppose that I'd propose f'r to enthrust him with a lofty
constichoochinal mission if he on'y kilt wan man. Me
notions iv th' jooties iv public office is far higher thin
that, I thank hivin. Besides in th' case ye speak iv
'twas justifiable homicide. He had ast th' man to
dhrink with him. No, sir, I have examined his record
carefully an' I find him fully equipped f'r anny
emergency. He niver misses. He's th' man f'r th'
place, th' quick dhrawin', readily passionate, hammer-
less gun firin' Terror iv th' Great Desert.'

" But th' Sinit didn't approve iv him. Th' sinitor fr'm Matsachoosetts, where human life is held so
cheap that no wan thinks iv takin' it, pro-tested
again' him, an' 'twas fin'lly discovered that early in
his career he'd been caught runnin' off a bunch iv
cows an' pushed into jail, an' that was too much f'r
th' hon'rable body, hardly wan mimber iv which has
iver been caught. So they give Jake th' go-by.

" But it'll come out all right in th' end. Th' prisidint knows what th' West wants an' he 'll get it f'r
thim. Th' West is no effete community, where th'
folks likes a quiet book-keepin' life, an early supper,
a game iv cards, lock th' windy, wind th' clock an' so
to bed. That may do f'r th' East. But in th' West,
we demand Sthrenuse Life an' Sudden Death. We're
people out here on th' des'late plains where th' sun
sets pink acrost th' gray desert an' th' scorpion clings
to th' toe. We don't want pianny tuners or plasther
saints to govern us. We want men who go to bed

with their spurs on, an' can break a gun without spikin' their thumbs. We'll have thim too. Undher precedin' administhrations, th' job wint to th' la-ads with no more qualifications thin is needed to run a dairy lunch. Some iv th' bes' places in th' West is held be th' poorest shots, while men capable iv th' mos' sthrikin' gun plays is left to devote their talents to private functions. An' they call that th' merit system! I expict th' time is near at hand whin justice will be done thim worthy citizens. At prisint whin a man is needed f'r a govermint office, he is called on to set down with a sheet of pa-aper an' a pot iv ink an' say how manny times eight-an'-a-half will go into a line dhrawn fr'm th' base iv th' hypothenoose, an' if he makes th' answer bright an' readable, they give him a place administherin' th' affairs iv a proud people that cudden't tell a hypothenoose fr'm a sealion. But whin things gets goin' right undher this administhration, th' civil sarvice commission consistin' iv th' Hon. Bill Cody, th' Hon. Texas Jack, an' th' Hon. Bat Masterson will put th' boys through an examination that'll bring out all there is in thim. I'm preparin' a pa-aper f'r an examination iv candydates f'r sup'rintindint iv th' Smithsonyan Institoot:

" 1. Describe a round-up.

" 2. Name five iv th' best brands (a) cattle (b) whiskey, ye have used.

" 3. Afther makin' a cinch, is it proper f'r to always kick th' critter in th' stomach or on'y whin ye feel like it?

"* 4. Undher what circumstances shud a Mexican not be shot, and if so, why?

" 5. How long shud a tinderfoot dance befure he is entitled to live?

" 6. Name eighty reasons f'r dhrawin' a gun.

" 7. State ye'er opinyion iv sheep men.

" 8. Write a brief account iv th' life an' death iv Billy th' Kid.

" Iv coorse, Hinnissy, this is on'y a part iv th' exercise. They'll be practical tests as well. Th' iligible list'll be taken out into th' yard an' required to shoot at movin' an' stationary targets, at pedesthreens an' horsemen, fr'm th' pocket, fr'm th' hip, over th' shouldher, fr'm a window with a sawed-off shot gun, an' so on. They'll be required to bust a buckin' bronc, cut out a steer fr'm th' herd without stampedin' th' rest, lassoo movin' objects an' give other exhibitions iv science. An' th' la-ad that wins out'll have to defind his job again' all comers f'r a month.

" I want to see this day. We're a nation iv hayroes, an' none but hayroes shud enjye th' spoil. Thin we'll read that th' Hon. Mike McCorker has been appinted Ambassadure to England: ' Mike is wan iv th' mos' detarmined statesmen between Rapid City an' Rawlins. His early life was spint in seclusion, owin' to a little diff'rence about a horse, but he had no sooner appeared in public life thin he made his mark on th' marshal iv Red Gulch. He applied himsilf to his chosen career with such perseverance an' so thrue an aim that within two years he had risen to th' head iv his pro-fission, a position that he has since held without interruption excipt durin' th' peryod whin th' Hon. Grindle H. Gash shelled him f'r three days with a howitzer. His remarkable night attack on that gallant but sleepy statesman will not soon be f'rgotten. A great ovation will be given Bill whin he pulls his freight f'r th' coort iv Saint James. Some iv th' boys is loadin' up f'r it already, an' near all th' Chinese has moved into th' hills. Ambassadure Gash was a Rough Rider durin' th' late Cubian War.

" ' Th' appintment iv Judge Rufus Flush to be Chief Justice iv th' United States Supreme Coort is hailed with delight be all citizens iv New Mexico. Judge Flush is th' recognized authority on gun shot wounds an' lynch law in th' Southwest, besides bein' in private life a pretty handy man with knife or gun himsilf. He was wan iv th' first men up San Joon Hill on th' mim'rable day.

" ' Th' sicrety iv state was visited yisterdah be throop B iv th' Rough Riders, includin' th' sicrety iv th' threesury, th' postmasther gin'ral, nine disthrick judges, forty postmasthers, an' wan hundherd an' eight collictors iv intarnal rivinoo. Th' conversation was informal, but it is undhershtud that th' advisability iv an excursion to Boston to shoot up th' anti-impeeryalist saloons was discussed. Th' prisidint dhropped in durin' th' conference an' greeted all prisint be their first name, which is Bill. There was some good-natured chaff as to which iv th' gintlemen was first at th' top iv San Joon Hill befure th' meetin' broke up. Th' postmasther gin'ral is sufferin' fr'm a slight knife wound.' "

# Bad Men from the West

" Ar-re all th' people West iv th' park shootin'
men? " asked Mr. Hennessy timidly.

" I think so," said Mr. Dooley, " but a man that's
been out there tells me not.  He says annywan but
an Englishman cud go fr'm wan end iv th' West to
th' other without carryin' a gun, an' that people that
kill each other are not considhered rayspictable in
Tucson anny more thin they wud be in Eysther Bay,
but that they are mostly dhrunk men an' th' like iv
that.  Th' towns, he says, is run be fellows that sell
ribbons, milk, yeast, spool thread an' pills an' pull
teeth an' argye little foolish law suits, just as th'
towns down here are run, an' th' bad men are more
afraid iv thim thin they are iv each other.  He says
there are things doin' out West that niver get into
th' dime novels, an' that whin people lose their lives
they do it more often in a saw mill or a smelter thin
in a dance hall.  He says so but I don't believe him."

" I suppose," said Mr. Hennessy, " a man iv me
peaceable disposition wud niver get a job."

" Make a repytation," said Mr. Dooley.  " Buy
a gun."

# European Intervention

"TH' question befure th' house is," said Mr. Dooley, "which wan iv th' Euro-peen powers done mos' f'r us in th' Spanish war."

"I thought they were all again' us," said Mr. Hennessy.

"So did I," said Mr. Dooley, "but I done thim an injustice. I was crool to thim crowned heads. If it hadn't been f'r some wan power, an' I can't make out which it was, th' Cubians to-day wud be opprissed be th' Casteel instead iv th' Beet Sugar Thrust an' th' Filipinos'd be shot be Mausers instead iv Krag-Jorgensens. Some wan power shtretched out its hand an' said, 'No. No,' it said, 'thus far but no farther. We will not permit this misguided but warrum-hearted little people to be crushed be th' ruffyan power iv Spain,' it said. 'Niver,' it said, 'shall his-thry record that th' United States iv America, nestlin' there in its cosy raypublic fr'm th' Atlantic to th' Passyfic, was desthroyed an' th' hurtage iv liberty that they robbed fr'm us wasted because we did not give thim support,' it says. An' so whin th' future looked darkest, whin we didn't know whether th' war wud last eight or be prolonged f'r tin weary, thragic minyits, whin it seemed as though th' Spanish fleet wud not sink unless shot at, some kindly power was silently comfortin' us an' sayin' to itsilf: 'I do so

hope they'll win, if they can.' But I don't know which
wan it was.

" At first I thought it was England. Whiniver ye
hear iv anny counthry helpin' us, ye think it is England. That's because England has helped us so much
in th' past. Says Lord Cranburne in reply to a
question in th' House iv Commons: ' I am reluctantly
foorced be mesilf to blushin'ly admit that but f'r us,
people on their way to China to-day wud be gettin'
up an' lookin' over th' side iv th' ship an' sayin',
" This is where America used to be." Whin war was
first discussed, mesilf an' th' rest iv th' fam'ly met
an' decided that unless prompt action was took, our
cousins an' invistmints acrost th' sea wud be damaged
beyond repair, so we cabled our ambassadure to go at
wanst to th' White House an' inform th' prisidint
that we wud regard th' war as a crool blot on civilization an' an offinse to th' intillygince iv mankind. I
am glad to say our inthervintion was iffycacious.
War was immeedjately declared. I will not tell ye
how high our hearts beat as we r-read th' news fr'm
day to day. Ye know. I will on'y say that we in-
sthructed our ambassadure to do ivrything in his power
to help our kinsmen an' he faithfully ixicuted his
ordhers. He practically lived at th' White House
durin' th' thryin' peeryod, an' his advice to th' prisidint such as: " If ye go on with this binnyficint war
th' United Powers will knock ye'er head off," or " I
think I can secure fav'rable terms fr'm th' Powers if
ye will abdicate in favor iv a riprisintative iv th' house
iv Bourbon an' cede New England to Spain," done

more thin annything else to put heart into th' American foorces. I will add that durin' this time we was
approached be an ambassadure iv wan iv th' powers
who ast us to inthervene. I will not say which power
it was, excipt that it was Austhrya-Hungary an' I'm
previnted be th' obligations iv me office fr'm min-
tionin' what powers was behind th' move beyond hint-
in' that they was as follows: Germany, France,
Rooshya, It'ly, China, Turkey, Monaco, San Marino,
Boolgahrya, Montinaygro, Booloochistan an' Per-
shya. Pah's reply to th' ambassadure was: " I will
do all I can " as he kicked him down stairs. It ill
becomes me to say what else we done f'r that home iv
freedom—an' hiven knows I wisht it'd stay there an'
not be wandherin' over th' face iv th' wurruld—but
I'm not proud iv me looks an' I will remark that Tiddy
Rosenfelt was capably directed be th' iditors iv England, thim hearts iv oak, that th' American navy was
advised be our mos' inargetic corryspondints an'
that, to make th' raysult certain, we lint a few British
gin'rals to th' Spanish. Cud frindship go farther?
As they say in America: " I reckon, be gosh, not." '

" Well, whin I read this speech I was prepared
to hang th' medal f'r savin' life on th' breasts iv th'
hands acrost th' sea where there's always plinty iv
hooks f'r medals. But th' nex' day, I picks up th'
pa-aper an' sees that 'twas not England done it but
Germany. Yes, sir, 'twas Germany. Germany was
our on'y frind. They was a time whin it looked as
though she was goin' to shoot at us to keep us fr'm
th' consequences iv our rash act. They'se nawthin'

Germany wudden't do for or to a frind. Yes, it was Germany. But it was France, too. La Belle France was there with a wurrud iv encouragemint an' a glance iv affection out iv her dark eyes that kep' growin' darker as th' war proceeded. An' it was Rooshya. Whin th' Czar heerd iv th' war, th' first thing he said was: ' I'm so sorry. Who is th' United States?' An' 'twas It'ly an' Booloochistan an' Boolgahrya an' even Spain. Spain was our frind till th' war was over. Thin she rounded on us an' sold us th' Ph'lippines.

" They was all our frinds an' yet on'y wan iv thim was our frind. How d'ye make it out, Hinnissy? Hogan has a sayin' that onaisy lies th' head that wears a crown, but it seems to be as aisy f'r some iv thim as f'r th' mos' dimmycratic American. But whoiver it was that saved us I'm thankful to thim. It won't do f'r ye to look at th' map an' say that th' pow'rful proticetin' nation wud be hardly big enough f'r a watch charm f'r a man fr'm Texas, or that Europeen assistance f'r America is about as useful as a crutch f'r a foot-runner. But f'r th' inthervention iv our unknown frind, we'd've been annihilated. Th' powers wud've got together an' they wud've sint over a fleet that wud've been turrble if it didn't blow up an' th' crews didn't get sea-sick. They wud've sint an irresistible ar-rmy; an' fin'ly if all else failed, they wud rayfuse food. That's goin' to be th' unsixpicted blow iv anny war that th' parishes iv Europe wages again' us. They will decline to eat. They will turn back our wheat an' pork an' short rib sides. They'll starve us out. If left to their own resoorces, Europe cud outstarve America in a month."

"I'm not afraid iv thim," said Mr. Hennessy. "Whin I was a young man, I cud take a runnin' jump acrost Germany or France, an' as f'r England we'd hardly thrip over it in th' dark."

"Perhaps ye're right," said Mr. Dooley. "But if all thim gr-reat powers, as they say thimsilves, was f'r to attack us, d'ye know what I'd do? I'll tell ye. I'd blockade Armour an' Comp'ny an' th' wheat ilivators iv Minnysoty. F'r, Hinnissy, I tell ye, th' hand that rocks th' scales in th' grocery store, is th' hand that rules th' wurruld."

# The Philippine Peace

# THE PHILIPPINE PEACE

"'TIS sthrange we don't hear much talk about th' Ph'lippeens," said Mr. Hennessy.

"Ye ought to go to Boston," said Mr. Dooley. "They talk about it there in their sleep. Th' raison it's not discussed annywhere else is that ivrything is perfectly quiet there. We don't talk about Ohio or Ioway or anny iv our other possissions because they'se nawthin' doin' in thim parts. Th' people ar-re goin' ahead, garnerin' th' products iv th' sile, sindin' their childher to school, worshipin' on Sundah in th' churches an' thankin' Hiven f'r th' blessin's iv free govermint an' th' pro-tiction iv th' flag above thim.

"So it is in th' Ph'lippeens. I know, f'r me frind Gov'nor Taft says so, an' they'se a man that undher-stands con-tintmint whin he sees it. Ye can't thrust th' fellows that comes back fr'm th' jools iv th' Passyfic an' tells ye that things ar-re no betther thin they shud be undher th' shade iv th' cocoanut palm be th' blue wathers iv th' still lagoon. They mus' be satisfied with our rule. A man that isn't satisfied whin he's had enough is a glutton. They're satisfied an' happy an' slowly but surely they're acquirin' that love f'r th' govermint that floats over thim that will make thim good citizens without a vote or a right to thrile be jury. I know it. Guv'nor Taft says so.

[ 115 ]

" Says he: ' Th' Ph'lippeens as ye have been tol'
be me young but speechful frind, Sinitor Bivridge,
who was down there f'r tin minyits wanst an' spoke
very highly an' at some lenth on th' beauties iv th'
scenery, th' Ph'lippeens is wan or more iv th' beautiful jools in th' diadem iv our fair nation.  Formerly
our fair nation didn't care f'r jools, but done up
her hair with side combs, but she's been abroad some
since an' she come back with beautiful reddish goolden
hair that a tiara looks well in an' that is betther f'r
havin' a tiara.  She is not as young as she was.  Th'
simple home-lovin' maiden that our fathers knew has
disappeared an' in her place we find a Columbya,
gintlemen, with machurer charms, a knowledge iv
Euro-peen customs an' not averse to a cigareet.  So
we have pinned in her fair hair a diadem that sets
off her beauty to advantage an' holds on th' front iv
th' hair, an' th' mos' lovely pearl in this ornymint is thim sunny little isles iv th' Passyfic.  They
are almost too sunny f'r me.  I had to come
away.

" ' To shift me language suddintly fr'm th' joolry
counther an' th' boodore, I will say that nawthin'
that has been said even be th' gifted an' scholarly
sinitor, who so worthily fills part iv th' place wanst
crowded be Hendricks an' McDonald, does justice to
th' richness iv thim islands.  They raise unknown
quantities iv produce, none iv which forchnitly can
come into this counthry.  All th' riches iv Cathay,
all th' wealth iv Ind, as Hogan says, wud look like
a second morgedge on an Apache wickeyup compared

with th' untold an' almost unmintionable products iv
that gloryous domain. Me business kept me in
Manila or I wud tell ye what they are. Besides some
iv our lile subjects is gettin' to be good shots an'
I didn't go down there f'r that purpose.

" ' I turn to th' climate. It is simply hively. No
other wurrud describes it. A white man who goes
there seldom rayturns unless th' bereaved fam'ly in-
sists. It is jus' right. In winter enough rain, in
summer plinty iv heat. Gin'rally speakin' whin that
throphical sky starts rainin' it doesn't stop till it's
impty, so th' counthry is not subjected to th' sudden
changes that afflict more northerly climes. Whin it
rains it rains; whin it shines it shines. Th' wather
frequently remains in th' air afther th' sun has been
shinin' a month or more, th' earth bein' a little overcrowded with juice an' this gives th' atmosphere
a certain cosiness that is indescribable. A light
green mould grows on th' clothes an' is very becomin'.
I met a man on th' boat comin' back who said 'twas
th' finest winter climate in th' wurruld. He was be
profission a rubber in a Turkish bath. As f'r th' sum-
mers they are delicious. Th' sun doesn't sit aloft
above th' jools iv th' Passyfic. It comes down an'
mingles with th' people. Ye have heard it said th'
isles was kissed be th' sun. Perhaps bitten wud be
a betther wurrud. But th' timprachoor is frequently
modified be an eruption iv th' neighborin' volcanoes
an' th' inthraduction iv American stoves. At night
a coolin' breeze fr'm th' crather iv a volcano makes
sleep possible in a hammock swung in th' ice-box. It

is also very pleasant to be able to cuk wan's dinner within wan.

" ' Passin' to th' pollytical situation, I will say it is good. Not perhaps as good as ye'ers or mine, but good. Ivry wanst in a while whin I think iv it, an iliction is held. Unforchnitly it usually happens that those ilicted have not yet surrindhered. In th' Ph'lippeens th' office seeks th' man, but as he is also pursooed be th' sojery, it is not always aisy to catch him an' fit it on him. Th' counthry may be divided into two parts, pollytically,—where th' insurrection continues an' where it will soon be. Th' brave but I fear not altogether cheery army conthrols th' insurrected parts be martiyal law, but th' civil authorities are supreme in their own house. Th' diff''rence between civil law an' martiyal law in th' Ph'lippeens is what kind iv coat th' judge wears. Th' raysult is much th' same. Th' two branches wurruks in perfect harmony. We bag thim in th' city an' they round thim up in th' counthry.

" ' It is not always nicessry to kill a Filipino American right away. Me desire is to idjacate thim slowly in th' ways an' customs iv th' counthry. We ar-re givin' hundherds iv these pore benighted haythen th' well-known, ol'-fashioned American wather cure. Iv coorse, ye know how 'tis done. A Filipino, we'll say, niver heerd iv th' histhry iv this counthry. He is met be wan iv our sturdy boys in black an' blue iv th' Macabebee scouts who asts him to cheer f'r Abraham Lincoln. He rayfuses. He is thin placed upon th' grass an' given a dhrink, a baynit bein' fixed in

[ 118 ]

his mouth so he cannot reject th' hospitality. Undher th' inflooence iv th' hose that cheers but does not inebriate, he soon warrums or perhaps I might say swells up to a ralization iv th' granjoor iv his adoptive counthry. One gallon makes him give three groans f'r th' constitchoochion. At four gallons, he will ask to be wrapped in th' flag. At th' dew pint he sings Yankee Doodle. Occasionally we run acrost a stubborn an' rebellyous man who wud sthrain at me idee iv human rights an' swallow th' Passyfic Ocean, but I mus' say mos' iv these little fellows is less hollow in their pretintions. Nachrally we have had to take a good manny customs fr'm th' Spanyard, but we have improved on thim. I was talkin' with a Spanish gintleman th' other day who had been away f'r a long time an' he said he wudden't know th' counthry. Even th' faces iv th' people on th' sthreets had changed. They seemed glad to see him. Among th' mos' useful Spanish customs is reconcenthration. Our reconcenthration camps is among th' mos' thickly popylated in th' wurruld. But still we have to rely mainly on American methods. They are always used fin'lly in th' makin' iv a good citizen, th' garotte sildom.

" ' I have not considhered it advisable to inthrajooce anny fads like thrile be jury iv ye'er peers into me administhration. Plain sthraight-forward dealin's is me motto. A Filipino at his best has on'y larned half th' jooty iv mankind. He can be thried but he can't thry his fellow man. It takes him too long. But in time I hope to have thim thrained to a pint where they can be good men an' thrue at th' inquest.

"'I hope I have tol' ye enough to show ye that th' stories iv disordher is greatly exaggerated. Th' counthry is pro-gressin' splindidly, th' ocean still laps th' shore, th' mountains are there as they were in Bivridge's day, quite happy apparently; th' flag floats free an' well guarded over th' govermint offices, an' th' cherry people go an' come on their errands—go out alone an' come back with th' throops. Ivrywhere happiness, contint, love iv th' shtep-mother counthry, excipt in places where there ar-re people. Gintlemen, I thank ye.'

"An' there ye ar-re, Hinnissy. I hope this here lucid story will quite th' waggin' tongues iv scandal an' that people will let th' Ph'lippeens stew in their own happiness."

"But sure they might do something f'r thim," said Mr. Hennessy.

"They will," said Mr. Dooley. "They'll give thim a measure iv freedom."

"But whin?"

"Whin they'll sthand still long enough to be measured," said Mr. Dooley.

# Soldier and Policeman

"TH' life iv a sojer though gloryous is hard," said Mr. Dooley. "Here's me frind, Gin'ral Fustian, wan iv th' gallantest men that has come out iv Kansas since Stormy Jordan's day, has been called down f'r on'y suggistin' that Sinitor Hoar an' th' rest iv thim be hanged be th' heels. I'm with th' gallant gin'ral mesilf. I'm not sure but he'd like to hang me, though as ye know, me opinyions on th' Ph'lippeens is varyous an' I don't give a dam ayether way. If he runs me to earth I on'y ast him as a fellow pathrite that he won't give me th' wather cure. Th' very thought iv it makes me flesh creep.

"But th' prisidint called him down. Afther th' publication iv th' fifteenth speech whin ivry colledge pro-fissor in this broad an' fair land was undher sintince iv death fr'm th' gin'ral, th' prisidint wrote to him sayin': 'Dear Fred: Me attintion has been called to ye'er pathriotic utthrances in favor iv fryin' Edward Atkinson on his own cuk shtove. I am informed be me advisers that it can't be done. It won't fry beans. So I am compilled be th' reg'lations iv war to give ye a good slap. How ar-re ye, ol' commerade-in-arms? Ye ought to 've seen me on th' top iv San Joon hill. Oh, that was th' day! Iver, me dear Fred, reprovingly but lovingly, T. Rosenfelt,

late colonel First United States Volunteers Calv'ry,
betther known as th' Rough Riders, an' ex-officio prisidint iv th' United States.' That was wan f'r Fred.
I wisht th' same cud be handed to Gin'ral Miles. Ivry
time he opins his mouth, if 'tis on'y to say 'tis a fine
day—which I must say is seldom—all they do to him
is to break his back.

" 'Tis a hard life, a sojer's, but a gloryous wan.  I
wisht me father had enthered me f'r a martial career
instead iv tachin' me be precipt an' example to be
quick on me feet.  In these days whin a man gets to
be a gin'ral because he's been a long time a doctor
or because he's suprrised a naygur rite, 'tis me that
wud go boundin' up to th' top iv th' laddher.

" ' Janooary wan, Private Dooley distinguished
himsilf at th' Battle iv Ogoowan in th' island iv Sa-
mar be rushin' out in a perfect hell iv putty-balls,
rice, arrers, an' harsh cries, an' seizin' th' gin'ral iv
th' Tamalese an' batin' him over th' head with his own
bean-blower.

" ' Janooary twinty: Colonel Dooley iv th' hun-
derth an' eighth Macabebee scouts yisterdah administhered th' best an' muddyest part iv th' Gingong
river to Gin'ral Alfico Bim in th' prisince iv a large
an' smilin' audjeence. Th' ribil had rayfused to com-
municate his plans to th' gallant colonel, but afther
he had had sufficient irrigation his conversation was
more extinded.  So was th' gin'ral.

" ' Feb'ry eighth: Gin'ral Dooley, th' hayro iv th'
Ph'lippeens who is at home with a large spleen which
he got into him in our beautiful island possissions made

a speech before th' Locoed club las' night. He said
we shud niver give up th' Ph'lippeens which had been
wathered be some iv th' best blood in our land—he
might say all. He didn't know much about th' constichoochion, but fr'm what he heerd about it fr'm a
man in his rig'mint who cud spell, it wasn't intinded
f'r use out iv coort. He thought no wan shud be
ilicted to congress undher th' rank iv major. There
was much talk iv pro-gress in lithrachoor an' science
which he was in favor iv hangin'. All th' army
needed was rope enough an' all wud be well. Th'
Supreme Coort was all right but if ye wanted justice
hot out iv th' oven, ye shud see it administhered be
three or four laughin' sub-alturns on th' stumps iv
threes, jus' afther lunch.

" ' March eighth: Prisidint Dooley, chafin' at th'
delay in th' Sinit requirin' all civilyans to submit
their opinyons on th' tariff to th' neighborin' ray-
cruitin' sergeant wanst a week, wint over to th' cap-
itol this mornin' with a file iv sojers an' arristed
th' anti-administhration foorces who are now locked
up in th' barn back iv th' White House. Th' prisidint was severely lacerated be Sinitor Tillman durin'
th' encounther.'

" Yes, sir, I'd like to be a sojer. I want to be a
military man. An' yet I niver wanted to be a polisman. 'Tis sthrange, too, f'r if ye think it over they
ain't th' lot iv diff''rence between th' mos' ordhinry,
flat-footed elbow that iver pulled wan leg afther another to mornin' roll-call an' th' gr-reatest gin'ral
that iver wint through a war behind a band on a

horse. They both belong to th' race iv round-headed men. Whin ye lenthen th' head iv a man or dog, ye rayjooce his courage. That's thrue iv all but th' bull-tarryer an' th' Turk. Both iv thim fight like th' divvle. Th' jooties is much th' same but th' polisman's is harder. Th' polisman has to fight night an' day but th' sojer on'y wanst a month. A man's got to be five foot nine to get on th' foorce. He can be five foot eight an' get into th' army through West Pint, or three foot two an' get in through th' War Department. Didn't Mike Gilligan take more chances whin he wint up to th' patch where Red Starkey was holdin' th' fort with a Krupp gun an' took him be th' hand an' pivoted with him out iv a window, thin me frind Fearless Freddy win he assumed false whiskers, pretinded to be a naygur an' stole little Aggynaldoo out iv his flat? Ye wudden't expict a pathrolman to be promoted to be sergeant f'r kidnapin' an organ-grinder, wud ye? An' Gilligan didn't ask f'r lave iv absence an' go down town to th' Union Lague Club an' tell th' assembled mannyfactherers iv axle-grease what ought to be done with th' wather taxes. No, sir! What happened to Gilligan was at roll-call th' nex' mornin' th' Loot says: 'Officer Gilligan, in capturin' Starkey, ye reflicted gr-reat credit on this precinct an' ye'er own bringin' up. But I want ye to know, officer, that this important arrist is no excuse f'r ye goin' out an' loadin' ye'ersilf to th' joo-pint with Hannigan's paint. Th' nex' time ye miss pullin' ye'er box, I'll have ye up befure th' thrile boord. Put that in ye'er pipe an' smoke it, Mike Gilligan.' An' Gilligan blushed.

" No, sir, between th' two, th' polisman's life's th' hard wan. He can't rethreat f'r reinfoorcemints or surrindher with all th' honors iv war. If he surrin- dhers, he's kilt an' if he rethreats, his buttons comes off. He gets no soord fr'm Congress whin he brings in Starkey be th' burnin' hair iv his head. If he's pro- moted to sergeant, he's sure to be bounced be th' first rayform administhration. He takes his ordhers, car- ries his stick iv timber up hill an' down dale undher th' gleamin' stars, has nawthin' to say but ' Move on there, now,' an' if his foot slips another round- headed man pushes him into a cell an' a impartyal jury iv men that's had throuble with th' polis befure convicts him heartily.

" Now, suppose Gilligan's father whin he was young had looked him over an' said : ' Agathy, Michael's head is per-fictly round. It's like a base- ball. 'Tis so pecoolyar. An' he has a fightin' face. 'Tis no good thryin' to tache him a thrade. Let's make a sojer iv him.' An' he wint into th' army. If he'd done there what he's done in th' patch, 'tis Gin- 'ral Gilligan he'd be be this time—Gin'ral Gilligan stormin' th' heights iv San Joon Hill; Gin'ral Mike Gilligan suspindin' th' haveas corpus in th' Ph'lip- peens an' th' anti-impeeryalists at home; Gin'ral Mike Gilligan capturin' Aggynaldoo, an' he'd do it with bare hands an' without th' aid iv a mustache; Gin'ral Mike Gilligan abolishin' th' third reader; Gin'ral Mike Gilligan discoorsin' to th' public on

' Books I have niver read: Series wan, th' Histhry iv
th' United States.' If his foot slips an' he grows
a little cross with a pris'ner iv war on th' way to th'
station an' dhrops his soord or his club on th' top
iv him, is he up befure th' judge an' thried be a jury
iv his peers? Officer Mike, yes; Gin'ral Mike, no.
Gin'ral Mike has no peers. He raceives a letther
notifyin' him that he has broken a human skull divine
an' th' reg'lations iv th' army an' must be thried.
' Who will me brave frind have go through with this
here austere but hail-fellow inquiry?' ' Oh, annywan will do. Anny iv th' gallant lift'nants iv me
brigade will do,' says Gin'ral Mike. So th' Gin'ral is
put on thrile an' a frind iv his addhresses th' coort.
' Gintlemen,' says he, ' th' question befure th' coort
is not so much did our gallant leader hammer th' coon
as whether our flag wanst stuck up where we have
wathered so many precious citizens shall iver come
down. (Th' coort: ' No, no!') That's th' pint.
What do th' people at home who know nawthin' about
this here war, excipt what we tell thim, what do they
mane be subjectin' this here hayro, gray an' bent
with infirmities but pretty spry at that, to this
ignominy? He has fought f'r thim an' what have
they done f'r him? In more thin wan year he has
on'y risen fr'm th' rank iv captain to brigadier gin-
'ral an' his pay is less thin twinty times what it was.
(Here th' coort weeps.) I ast ye, I ast ye, ye fine
little boys, is it meet an' proper, nay, is it meat an'
dhrink f'r us, to punish him?'

  " An' th' coort puts th' vardict iv acquittal in th'

[ 128 ]

shape iv th' pop'lar song 'F'r he's a jolly good fellow' an' adds a ricommindation that Harvard colledge is gettin' too gay annyhow.

"That's th' diff'rence between sojer an' polisman. Why is it that th' fair sect wudden't be seen talkin' to a polisman, but if ye say 'Sojer' to thim, they're all out iv th' window but th' feet? I want to know."

"I can't tell," said Mr. Hennessy. "I heerd a frind iv Willum J. Bryan say we was in danger iv havin' thim run th' counthry like they do in—in Germany, d'ye mind."

"Niver fear," said Mr. Dooley. "There's too manny Gilligans not in th' ar-rmy f'r that."

# King Edward's Coronation

"NOW that th' king iv Great Britain an' Ireland, but Ireland don't know it, an' th' Dominyons beyond th' sea, f'r awhile, has been cawrnated," said Mr. Dooley, "we can raysume where we left off."

"So it has been done at last, has it?" said Mr. Hennessy.

"Yes," said Mr. Dooley, "in th' prisince iv th' mos' illusthrees iv his subjects, except me frind Whitelaw Reid, he was cawrnated las' Saturdah. 'Tis too bad it was put off. 'Twas got up, d'ye mind, f'r th' thrue an' staunch subjects on this side iv th' wather. Th' king didn't need it. He's been king all th' time. A lot iv us knew it. All he had to do anny time was to take his caubeen fr'm th' rack, but his subjects fr'm beyond th' sea wanted to see a cawrnation, an' they cudden't convaniently have wan here where th' counthry is still run be univarsal suffering an' there are a good manny shootin' gall'ries, an' annyhow he thought he'd like to keep on good terms with th' Captains iv Industhry f'r fear they might get mad an' put his furniture out into th' channel an' use th' island f'r storin' ex-prisidints. So he got up th' cawrnation. An' afther all, most iv thim didn't see it. They had to come home here where they were born an' lave th' land where they expict to die an' will, too, if they an' us have luck.

"But 'twas a gorgyous spicticle annyhow, Hinnissy. F'r weeks an' weeks some iv th' finest minds in Europe has been debatin' whether th' king shud stand on th' Earl iv Whinkie or th' markess iv Ballyhoo durin' th' ceremony. It was decided that th' honor shud go to th' noble earl, but that it was th' privilege iv th' noble markess that his majesty shud put his feet on his back whin he set down. Th' king ain't supposed to do annything f'r himsilf but go up an' be cawrnated. At ivry turn they must be a jook or somebody akelly as good to pull his tie sthraight, hand him his gloves, an' haul his coat down whin it gets up over th' collar. An' ivrybody cudden't do it, mind ye. It had to be done be th' right party, whose folks had done it f'r other kings. I've been readin' about it an' I've come to th' con-clusion, Hinnissy, that th' Scotch nobility is mos'ly dayscinded fr'm tailors.

"Annyhow, these here mighty questions was all decided accoordin' to th' rules iv th' game, whin wan day I read in th' pa-aper: ' Th' king dines with Wall sthreet magnates. Jools missin' fr'm th' crown.' Ye see, th' hat had not been out f'r a long time an' whin they come to get it fr'm th' box, 'twas found that manny iv th' vallyable gems in th' band was missin'. I don't know whether 'tis thrue or not, but 'tis said that th' ancesthors iv th' prisint king, bein' hard up, was used to pick a jool out iv th' hat iv a Saturdah night an' go down to Mose at th' corner an' get something on it. An' whin times was slack an' th' ponies backward, they cudden't get th' jools out, so they cut a piece fr'm th' window an' pasted it in. It looked f'r awhile as though th' king wud have to be cawrnated be a glazier. They cudden't find th' tickets high or low. It wudden't do to cawrnate him in a glass hat, an' there was gr-reat thribylations, but Pierpont Morgan come along at th' right moment an' give thim a handful iv his unimportant jools an' th' hat was properly decorated. Fr'm that time on we saw that if we were to get th' worth iv our money, we'd have to do th' job oursilves, an' ivrybody turned in to help our depindant cousins. Andhrew Carnaygie lint Wistminsther Abbey which was superbly dicorated with tapestries lint be J. Pierpont Morgan; Yerkes lint thim th' sthreets; Frohman th' theatres; th' American syndicate give thim th' use iv th' river, an' a hundherd thousand lile American hearts an' lungs lint thim a pathriotic howl that made th' king jump ivry time he heerd it.

"An' th' American duchesses! Were they there? Look in th' pa-apers. I sometimes wondher whin I read th' palajeems iv our liberties whether an English nobleman iver marries at home. Is it a law that prevints thim fr'm marryin' thim fresh-faced, clear-eyed daughters iv ol' Albion or is it fear? Annyhow, th' American duchesses is about all there is to it in London. They were at th' cawrnation, ye bet. They were th' cawrnation. They bore th' thrain iv th' queen. No wan can lift a thrain betther or higher thin a free-born American lady. At th' side iv her

majesty walked th' beautiful Duchess iv Binkie-
whistle, born Lucy Hicks iv Dobbs Ferry. Th'
Duchess' father an' mother come over las' week with
their respictive fam'lies, an' it is undhershtud that
wan iv th' happiest ivints iv th' whole glad cawrnation season was th' determination iv Ma Hicks to devote her alimony intire to rebuildin' th' ancesthral
mansion iv th' jook. Pa Hicks, not to be outdone, announced that he wud add th' rent derived fr'm th'
ancesthral mansion iv th' duchess, which is now used
as a livery stable.

" An' so th' gr-reat ivint come off. I won't describe it to ye. It's been done betther thin I cud do it
be a fearless press. Ye know ye'ersilf how th' pro-cission winded its way through th' sthreets ; how Wistminsther Abbey was crowded with peers an' peeresses,
an' what a mighty shout wint up fr'm Willum
Waldorf Astor whin he come in an' sat on his hat
near th' dure. It was all right. First come th' pre-
lates backin' to'rd th' althar. Thin all th' jooks
bowin' low. Thin th' queen, attinded be a bevy iv
American duchesses. Thin th' king lookin' ivry inch
a king—sixty-four be sixty-two in all. Thin th'
Rile Shoes, th' Rile Socks, th' Rile Collar an' Cuffs,
an' th' Rile Hat borne be th' hereditary Sockbearers,
Shoesters, Collariferios, an' th' High an' Magnificint
Lid-Lord (in chains). Suddenly all is silent. A
hush falls on th' assimblage, broken on'y be a low,
sad cry. Willum Waldorf Astor has fainted.

" An' so, says th' pa-aper, in th' prisince iv th'
mighty dead an' th' mighty near dead, among th'

surroundings that recalled th' days iv shivaree an' in an atmosphere full iv aristocratic assocyations, on account iv th' vintilation bein' poor, Albert Edward Ernest Pathrick Arthur, king, definder iv th' faith, put on his hat. Th' organ pealed off a solemn peal, th' cannons boomed, th' duchesses et hard-biled eggs out iv a paper bag, an' a pale man in silk tights wept over th' tomb iv Major Andhre. It was Joseph Chote. That night all Great Britain rejoiced, fr'm wan end iv Ireland to th' other th' lile popylace showed their joy an' th' sky was lit up be hundherds iv burnin' barns an' a salute iv forty-four guns was fired in th' County Kerry at a landlord's agent comin' home fr'm a ball.

"I hope he'll make a good king. I ain't so much down on kings as I used to be, Hinnissy. I ain't down on thim anny more because I don't invy thim, an' ye can't be down on anny man ye don't invy. 'Tis a hard job an' a thankless wan. A king nowadays is no more thin a hitchin' post f'r wan pollytician afther another. He ain't allowed to move himsilf, but anny crazy pollytician that ties up to him is apt to pull him out be th' roots. He niver has anny childhood. He's like th' breaker-boys in th' mines; he's put to wurruk larnin' his thrade as soon as he can walk. Whin it comes time f'r him to marry, th' prime ministher takes him out wan day an' says: ' There's th' on'y woman in th' wurruld f'r ye.' ' But I niver see her befure,' says th' unforchnit king. ' Ye'll see less iv her afther nex' week,' says th' prime ministher. ' Ye're goin' to marry her,' he says. An' he backs him up to th' bench where th' young lady sets an' inthrajooces thim an' they're marrid. Think iv havin' th' boord iv aldhermen silict a wife f'r ye an' ye'll know how th' king feels whin a warrant is sarved again' him to hook up with his cousin Agoosta Ann, a German lady who freckles aisily an' croshays neckties f'r a lift'nant in th' army. All his life long a king is bossed about like a hired girl in a boardin' house, an' he can't aven die without havin' a lot iv people runnin' in ivry tin minyits to ask has he done it yet so they can be on th' mark to holler ' God save th' king ' out iv th' front window th' moment th' flag falls. No, sir; I don't want to be a king an' whiniver I see a good fellow takin' th' job, I feel sorry f'r him. I know what he is up again'."

"I believe ye're no betther thin th' rest iv thim thraitors," said Mr. Hennessy.

"I'm diff'rent," said Mr. Dooley, calmly. "They helped him in an' I'd do annything in me power, now that he is king, to help him out."

# One Advantage of Poverty

"WELL, sir," said Mr. Dooley, "ye ought to be glad ye're not sick an' illusthrees at th' same time."

"How's that?" Mr. Hennessy demanded.

"Well, ye see," said Mr. Dooley, "suppose annything happens to ye now; a fellow counthryman dhrops a hammer on ye th' day afther th' picnic or ye'er di-gestion listens to a walkin' dillygate fr'm th' Union iv Microbes an' goes out on sthrike. Th' polisman on th' corner has th' usual suspicions among gintlemen an' hits ye over th' head an' calls th' wagon an' sinds ye home. Th' good woman wrings her hands an' calls Hiven to witness that if ye have a toothache ye wake th' neighborhood, an' slaps a mustard plasther on ye. If she comes back later an' finds ye haven't put th' sheet between ye an' th' plasther an' gone to sleep, she knows 'tis seeryous an' sinds f'r th' doctor. We continyoo to have doctors in what th' pa-apers calls th' outlyin' wards. They live above th' dhrug-store an' practice midicine on us. Th' physicians an' surgeons are all down town editin' th' pa-apers. Well, dock comes to ye afther awhile in a buggy. On th' way up he sets a broken leg, removes an arm, does a little something f'r th' city directhry, takes a dhrink, talks pollyticks with th' unhappy parent an' fin'lly lands at ye'er dure with

[ 141 ]

th' burglar's tools. Afther he's closed that dure th' secrets iv th' inner man is known on'y to him. No wan hears or wants to hear annything about it. Th' nex' time we see ye, ye come out lookin' pale an' emacyated an' much younger an' betther lookin' thin annywan iver raymimbers seein' ye, an' afther awhile ye obsarve that whin ye start to tell how manny stitches it took an' what ye see whin ye smelled th' dizzy sponge, ye'er frinds begin to sprint away. An' ye go back reluctantly to wurruk. Ye niver hear annywan say: ' Hinnissy is great comp'ny whin he begins to talk about his sickness.' I've seen men turn fr'm a poor, helpless, enthusyastic invalid to listen to a man talkin' about th' Nicaragoon canal.

" But with th' great 'tis far diff'rent. I've often thanked th' Lord that I didn't continyoo in pollytics whin I was cap'n iv me precinct, f'r with th' eyes iv all th' wurruld focussed, as Hogan says, on me, I cud niver injye th' pleasure iv a moment's sickness without people in far-off Boolgahrya knowin' whether me liver was on sthraight. Sickness is wan iv th' privileges iv th' poor man that he shares with no wan. Whin it comes kindly to him, th' four walls iv his room closes in on him like a tent, folks goes by on th' other side iv th' sthreet, th' rollin' mill disappears, an' with th' mornin' comes no honest day's tile. He lies there in blessid idleness an' no matther what's th' matther with him, he don't suffer half as much pain as he would in pursoot iv two dollars a day. I knowed a man wanst who used to take his vacations that way. Whin others wint off f'r to hunt what

Hogan calls th' finny monsthers iv th' deep, he become seeryously ill an' took to bed. It made him very sthrong.

" But suppose I hadn't resigned fr'm cap'n iv me precinct whin I was defeated. If annything had happened to me, ye'd pick up th' pa-apers an' see: ' Seeryous news about th' Cap'n iv th' twinty-sicond precinct iv th' sixth ward. He has brain fever. He has not. He got in a fight with a Swede an' had his ribs stove in. He fell out iv th' window iv a joolry store he was burglarizin' an' broke th' left junction iv th' sizjymoid cartilage. Th' throuble with th' Cap'n is he dhrinks too much. A man iv his age who has been a soak all his life always succumbs to anny throuble like hyperthroopily iv th' cranium. Docthor Muggers, dean iv th' Post Gradyate Vethrinary school iv Osteopathy says he had a similar case las' year in Mr. Hinnery Haitch Clohessy, wan iv th' best known citizens iv this city. Like th' Cap, Mr. Clohessy was a high liver, a heavy dhrinker, a gambler an' a flirt. Th' cases are almost identical. Owin' to th' code iv pro-fissional eethics Dr. Muggers cud not tell th' bereaved fam'ly what ailed Misther Clohessy, but it was undoubtedly his Past Life.'

" Thin come th' doctors. Not wan doctor, Hinnissy, to give ye a whiff out iv a towel an' make ye sleep f'r an hour an' wake up an' say ' I fooled ye. Whin do ye begin?' No, but all iv thim. They escort th' prisoner up th' sthreet in a chariot, an' th' little newsboys runs alongside sellin' exthry papers. ' Our night edition will print th' inside facts about

## Observations by Mr. Dooley

Cap Dooley's condition, an' th' Cap himsilf with a
cinematograph iv th' jolly proceedin's be Dock
Laparatonny.' What happens to th' criminal at
first is th' same as if he was a dacint, wurrukin' man.
But whin that is done, an' 'tis gettin' so aisy they
tell me they'se not much diff'rence between a good
clam-salesman an' a first-class surgeon, th' lithry
wurruk begins. Ye think 'tis all over whin ye say:
' Dock, put ye'er hand undher th' pillow an' take
what's there.' But not so. Th' assembled docks
adjourn to a large hall an' prepare th' story iv ' Cap
Dooley; a Stormy Career. Be wan who knows.'

" ' Upon seein' th' Cap, we at once diagnosed th'
case as peritclipalitickipantilitisitis, or chicken bone
in th' throat. Dr. Pincers operated, Dr. Smothers
administhered th' annysthetic, Dr. Hygeen opened
th' window, Dr. Anodyne turned on th' gas, Dr.
Aluompaine turned th' pitchers to th' wall, Dr.
Rambo looked out th' window, Docthors Peroxide,
Gycal, Cephalgern, Antipyreen an' Coltar took a
walk in th' park, an' Doctor Saliclate figured up th'
bill. As we have said we diagnosed th' case as above.
We can't raymimber th' name. It depinds on how
th' syllables came out iv th' hat. We were wrong,
although what we see whin we got in more thin made
up f'r th' error. We made a long incision fr'm th'
chin down an' another acrost an' not findin' what we
expicted, but manny things that ought to be kept fr'm
th' fam'ly, we put th' Cap back an' wint on. Th'
op'ration was a complete success. Th' wretch is
restin an' swearin' easily. We have given him a light

[ 144 ]

meal iv pickles an' antiseptic oats, an' surgical science havin' done its duty, mus' lave th' rest to Nature, which was not in th' consultation, bein' considhered be some iv us, slightly irregular.  (Signed)
Look at our names:

' Pincers,          Anodyne,           Peroxide,
  Smothers,        Coltar,            Antipyreen,
  Cepalgeen,       Alicompane,        Gycal,
  Hygeen,          Rambo,             Saliclate.'

" But that's nawthin'.  If ye think they'se annything ye wud like to keep up ye'er sleeve, look f'r
it in th' pa-apers.  ' Th' followin' facts is stated on
th' authority iv wan iv th' attindin' surgeons: Cap
Dooley cut up terribly undher th' chloryform, sing·
in' songs, swearin' an' askin' f'r Lucy.  His wife's
name is Annamariar.  She was in th' adjinin' room.
It seems they have had throuble.  Th' room was
poorly furnished.  Th' Cap's clothes was much worn
as was most iv him.  He must have led a shockin'
life.  It is doubtful if he will iver raycover f'r he
is very, very old.  He has been concealin' his age f'r
manny years.  He is a notoryous profligate, as was
well shown be th' view we had.  Th' flash light pitcher
iv th' Cap will appeal to all who know his inner
histhry.'

" An' there ye ar-re.  Think iv a man comin' out
in th' light iv day afther all that.  He can't get on
clothes enough to cover him.  He may bear himsilf
with a haughty manner, but he feels that ivry man
he meets knows more about him thin he knows himsilf.  Th' fellow on th' sthreet has been within th'

walls. He's sayin' to himsilf: ' Ye're a hollow sham composed akelly iv impaired organs an' antiseptic gauze.' To th' end iv his life, he'll niver be annything more thin an annytomical chart to his frinds. His privacy is over f'river, f'r what good can it do annywan, Hinnissy, to pull down th' blinds iv his bed room if ivrybody knows exactly th' size, shape an' location iv his spleen?

" No, sir, if I've got to be sick, give me th' ordhn'ry dacencies iv poverty. I don't want anny man to know anny more about me thin he can larn fr'm th' handiwork iv Marks, th' tailor, an' Schmitt, th' shoemaker, an' fr'm th' deceitful expression iv me face. If I have a bad heart, let him know it be me eyes. On me vest is written: ' Thus far an' no farther.' They'se manny a man on intimate terms with th' King iv England to-day that don't know anny more about me thin that I'm broadcloth on Sundah an' serge on week days. An' I don't intind they shall. I hide behind th' privileges iv me position an' say: ' Fellow-citizens, docks an' journalists, I cannot inthrajooce ye to th' Inner Man. He's a reecloose an' avarse to s'ciety. He's modest an' shy an' objects to callers. Ye can guess what kind iv man I am but I wudden't have ye know.' An' I can do that as long as I stay poor."

" I'm glad I'm poor," said Mr. Hennessy.

" It gives ye less to talk about but more to think about," said Mr. Dooley.

# The Fighting Word

"THAT man Bailey iv Texas f'r me ivry time," said Mr. Dooley.

"What's he been doin'?" asked Mr. Hennessy.

"He done me frind Biv'ridge iv Injyanny," said Mr. Dooley. "An' I'm f'r him f'r leader iv th' party. He's wan iv th' best two-handed orators in th' sinit or annywhere. He has a wondherful left an' his repartee with th' right is said to be very stingin'. He's inthrajooced th' sthrangle holt be means iv which th' debate can be suddenly cut off. He's me ideel leader.

"I want a leader who's got a good grip on public affairs an' men, who can take hold iv anny question or anny raypublican an' choke it or him till they're black in th' face. Bailey's th' boy. I followed Tillman f'r awhile, but he's gone back. He belongs to th' ol' school iv parlymintaryans, th' same that Jawn L. Sullivan belongs to. He's clever f'r an old 'un an' I'd be willin' to back him again anny raypublican in New England at catch-weights. His reply to Sinitor McLaurin was said to be wan iv th' quickest iver heerd since th' days iv Dan'l Webster. It laid open th' scalp. But they tell me Tillman's speeches is not what Hogan calls impromptchu. He rehearses thim ivry mornin' with a punchin'-bag. Bailey is more iv a nachral debater. No holds barred with him. Hand or fut, 'tis all th' same.

"What was it all about, says ye? Well, ye see this sinitor fr'm Injyanny, me frind Jeremiah Biv'ridge made a mos' insultin' remark to Misther Bailey. What did he say? I mustn't tell ye. No, no, 'tis too horrible. Well, if ye must hear it, close th' dure an' pull down th' blinds. Whisper! There! There ye have it. I blush to raypeat th' wurruds. To think that anny man shud so demean himsilf as to imagine such a thing, lave alone say it. But he did—right out in th' Sinit befure Hinnery Cabin Lodge. Oh, it was turr'ble. Here it is in th' pa-apers: 'Misther Biv'-ridge said th' st-t-m-nts iv th' hon'rable sinitor fr'm Texas was unw-r-nted.' Modesty where was thy blush? as Shakespere says. Now, th' sinitors iv th' United States is not aisily shocked. That's not th' way ye get into th' Sinit. Th' bright blush iv shame hasn't been used there more thin twice since th' war. Ye can say almost annything ye like to a sinitor. Ye can say he wanst stole a horse, that he's livin' undher an assumed name, that he was made be a thrust, that his on'y nourishment is beets, or that he belongs to New York s'ciety, an' th' Sinit will on'y yawn. But wanst even hint that his such-an'-such is so-an'-so (I will not repeat th' heejous wurruds) an' ye mus' hurry an' slip on th' brass knuckles, f'r they'se a slap comin' to ye.

"Here's what happened: 'Sinitor Bailey stepped quickly over Sinitors Hoar, Mason, Quay, an' others an' made f'r where Sinitor Biv'ridge was quitely

smokin' a cigar an' talkin' to himsilf. Sinitor Bailey
says: " Hon'rable sir, ye must withdraw that loath-
some insinooation again' me good name," he says. " I
have not led a pure life. No man has. I don't claim
to be anny betther thin others. But no wan befure has
iver said about me such things as these, an' if ye don't
take thim back at wanst, I'll kill ye, I'll choke ye, I'll
give ye a poke in th' eye," he says. " I cannot consint,"
says th' bold sinitor fr'm Injyanny, " I cannot consint
to haul back me epithet. It wud not be sinitoryal cour-
tesy," he says. " Thin," says Sinitor Bailey, " here
goes f'r an assault an' batthry." An' with a gesture
iv th' thrue orator, he seized him be th' throat. Th'
debate become gin'ral. Sinitor Spooner iv Wisconsin led f'r th' raypublicans an' Sinitor Morgan iv Ala-
bama counthered f'r th' dimmycrats. Sinitor Platt
made a very happy retort with a chair, to which Sinitor
Gorman replied with a sintintious cuspidor. Owin' to
th' excitin' nature iv th' debate on'y a few iv th' best
remarks reached th' gall'ry, wan iv thim, a piece iv
hard coal, layin' out a riprisintative iv th' Sultan iv
Zulu. At th' hospital he declared himsilf much imprissed. Durin' th' proceedin's Biv'ridge acted in
th' mos' gintlemanly an' even ladylike manner. His
face wore a smile iv complete sang fraud or pain, an'
he niver took his cigar fr'm his mouth wanst. Indeed,
it was siv'ral hours befure th' Havana cud be ex-
thracted be th' surgeon who was called in. While th'
debate was in progress, a pitcher iv Thomas Jefferson
was obsarved to give a slight moan an' turn its face
to th' wall. Th' Sinit thin took up routine business

an' th' janitor swept up th' hair an' neckties. Sinitor
Biv'ridge was not much hurt. Th' tinder outside iv
th' wind-pipe was somewhat bruised, but th' wurrukin'
inside is still intact.'

" 'Twas a pretty scene, Hinnissy, an' wan that
makes me proud iv Bailey f'r his courage in pouncin'
on his collague; iv Biv'ridge f'r th' manly self re-
sthraint an' rayspict f'r th' dignity iv th' Sinit that
par'lyzes a man's hands whin his wind is cut off; iv our
noble counthry that projooces such sturdy sons, iv th'
Sinit that brings thim together in a clinch an' iv mesilf because I wasn't there. I'm with Bailey. Bailey
f'r prisidint! Bailey or bust or choke!

" I'm not sure that if I was in th' same place I'd do
th' same thing. But I'm no statesman. Who am I
to say that what wudden't be manners in a bar-room
is not all right in th' Sinit? Diff'rent men has diff'rent
raisons f'r fightin'. Ivry man will fight. Ye can bet
on that. A brave man will fight because he is brave
an' a cow'rd because he is a cow'rd. All men will fight
an' all men will run. Some will fight befure they'll
run, but they'll run; some men will run befure they'll
fight, but they'll fight. They'se a pretty good fight
an' a pretty fast run in ivry man I know. Th' debate
in th' Sinit don't prove annything about th' merits iv
ayether pug. In some other circumstances, Biv'ridge
might have hunted Bailey up a three. It happened
to be Bailey's day.

" As I get on in years, I believe less in fightin'. 'Tis
a turr'ble thing to see th' aged an' infirm swingin' away
at each other. 'Tis so unscientific. I hate to think

iv a man with one leg in th' grave usin' th' other to thrip th' free foot iv a fellow aged. I'm glad Bailey an' Biv'ridge ar-re young men. What a scandal if Sinitor Cullom an' Sinitor Morgan shud mix it up! Wan iv th' things a man larns as he grows old is to dislike fightin'. He dislikes annything he can't do as well as he cud. I'm that way. But I wasn't always so. No, sir. They was a time whin I'd fight at th' dhrop iv a hat, f'r money or marbles or pool checks, f'r th' good name iv women or th' revarse, f'r political principles or unprincipled politics, f'r th' gate receipts, f'r me relligion, f'r th' look iv th' thing, because th' barkeeper heard what he said, because he whispered to her, f'r th' sacred theery that th' buildin's is higher in Chicago thin in New York, f'r th' fun iv th' thing, an' f'r th' Fight. That last's th' best iv all. A man that won't fight f'r th' fight itsilf is no rale fighter. I don't know what wud make me fight nowadays. I know lots iv things that wud make me want to fight, but I've larned to repress me desires. Me heart is full iv song but I've lost me voice. In me dhreams I'm always punchin' somebody's head. I shall niver f'rget th' night whin I put Jeffries out iv th' business with wan well-directed punch an' me in me bare feet, too. I can niver f'rget it f'r I fell out iv bed and bumped me head again' th' rocker iv a chair. But in me wakin' hours, I'm a man iv vi'lent impulses an' peaceful ray-sults. In a fight I'd be like a deef-mute in a debatin' s'ciety. But as I said, Hinnissy, they was a day whin th' lightest wurrud was an insult. Nowadays I say to mesilf: 'Considher th' soorce. How can such a low blaggard as that insult me? Jus' because some dhrunken wretch chooses to apply a foul epitaph to me, am I goin' to dignify him be knockin' him down in th' public sthreet an' p'raps not, an' gettin' th' head beat off me? No, sir. I will raymimber me position in th' community. I will pass on with a smile iv bitter contempt. Maybe I'd betther run a little.'

" Th' las' throuble I got into I begun to think iv th' new suit I had on an' I knew me warryor days was over. Whin a man raymimbers his clothes or his appearance in battle, 'tis high time f'r him to retire fr'm th' ring. Th' ca'm, almost deathlike smile that rests upon a man's face whin another man is cloutin' him about is on'y th' outward exprission iv something about two numbers up th' chest fr'm sea sickness. That's all I've got to say about fightin'. Ye can't lay down anny rules about it."

" Ye niver will go to th' Sinit with thim views," said Mr. Hennessy.

" I don't want to," said Mr. Dooley. " Some day th' Sinit will be pulled."

# Home Life of Geniuses

"**A** WOMAN ought to be careful who she marries," said Mr. Dooley.

"So ought a man," said Mr. Hennessy, with feeling.

"It don't make so much diff'rence about him," said Mr. Dooley. "Whin a man's marrid, he's a marrid man. That's all ye can say about him. Iv coorse, he thinks marredge is goin' to change th' whole current iv his bein', as Hogan says. But it doesn't. Afther he's been hooked up f'r a few months, he finds he was marrid befure, even if he wasn't, which is often th' case, d'ye mind. Th' first bride iv his bosom was th' Day's Wurruk, an' it can't be put off. They'se no groun's f'r dissolvin' that marredge, Hinnissy. Ye can't say to th' Day's Wurruk: 'Here, take this bunch iv alimony an' go on th' stage.' It turns up at breakfast about th' fourth month afther th' weddin' an' creates a scandal. Th' unforchnit man thries to shoo it off but it fixes him with its eye an' hauls him away fr'm the bacon an' eggs, while the lady opposite weeps and wondhers what he can see in annything so old an' homely. It says, 'Come with me, aroon,' an' he goes. An' afther that he spinds most iv his time an' often a good deal iv his money with th' enchantress. I tell ye what, Hinnissy, th' Day's Wurruk has broke up more happy homes thin comic opry. If th' coorts

wud allow it, manny a woman cud get a divorce on th'
groun's that her husband cared more f'r his Day's
Wurruk thin he did f'r her. ' Hinnissy varsus Hinnissy; corryspondint, th' Day's Wurruk.' They'd
be ividince that th' defindant was seen ridin' in a cab
with th' corryspondint, that he took it to a picnic, that
he wint to th' theaytre with it, that he talked about it
in his sleep, an' that, lost to all sinse iv shame, he even
escoorted it home with him an' inthrajooced it to his
varchoos wife an' innocint childher. So it don't make
much diff'rence who a man marries. If he has a job,
he's safe.

" But with a woman 'tis diff'rent. Th' man puts
down on'y part iv th' bet. Whin he's had enough iv
th' convarsation that in Union Park undher th' threes
med him think he was talkin' with an intellechool
joyntess, all he has to do is to put on his coat, grab up
his dinner pail an' go down to th' shops, to be happy
though marrid. But a woman, I tell ye, bets all she
has. A man don't have to marry but a woman does.
Ol' maids an' clargymen do th' most good in th'
wurruld an' we love thim f'r th' good they do. But
people, especially women, don't want to be loved that
way. They want to be loved because people can't
help lovin' thim no matther how bad they are. Th'
story books that ye give ye'er daughter Honoria all
tell her 'tis just as good not to be marrid. She reads
about how kind Dorothy was to Lulu's childher an' she
knows Dorothy was th' betther woman, but she wants
to be Lulu. Her heart, an' a cold look in th' eye iv
th' wurruld an' her Ma tell her to hurry up. Arly in

life she looks f'r th' man iv her choice in th' tennis rec-
ords; later she reads th' news fr'm th' militia encamp-
mint; thin she studies th' socyal raygisther; further
on she makes hersilf familyar with Bradsthreets' ray-
ports, an' fin'lly she watches th' place where life pre-
sarvers are hangin'.

"Now, what kind iv a man ought a woman to
marry? She oughtn't to marry a young man because
she'll grow old quicker thin he will; she oughtn't to
marry an old man because he'll be much older befure
he's younger; she oughtn't to marry a poor man because he may become rich an' lose her; she oughtn't to
marry a rich man because if he becomes poor, she can't
lose him; she oughtn't to marry a man that knows
more thin she does, because he'll niver fail to show it,
an' she oughtn't to marry a man that knows less because he may niver catch up. But above all things
she mustn't marry a janius. A flure-walker, perhaps; a janius niver.

"I tell ye this because I've been r-readin' a book
Hogan give me, about th' divvle's own time a janius
had with his fam'ly. A cap iv industhry may have
throuble in his fam'ly till there isn't a whole piece iv
chiny in th' cupboard, an' no wan will be the wiser f'r
it but th' hired girl an' th' doctor that paints th' black
eye. But ivrybody knows what happens in a janius'
house. Th' janius always tells th' bartinder. Besides he has other janiuses callin' on him, an' 'tis th'
business iv a janius to write about th' domestic
throubles iv other janiuses so posterity'll know what a
hard thing it is to be a janius. I've been readin' this

book iv Hogan's an' as I tell ye, 'tis about th' misery
a wretched woman inflicted on a pote's life.

" ' Our hayro,' says th' author, ' at this peeryod con-
thracted an unforchnit alliance that was destined to
cast a deep gloom over his career.   At th' age iv fifty,
afther a life devoted to th' pursoot iv such gayety as
janiuses have always found niciss'ry to solace their
avenin's, he marrid a young an' beautiful girl some
thirty-two years his junior.   This wretched crather
had no appreciation iv lithrachoor or lithry men.
She was frivolous an' light-minded an' ividintly considhered that nawthin' was rally lithrachoor that cudden't be thranslated into groceries.   Niver shall I f'r-
get th' expression iv despair on th' face iv this godlike
man as he came into Casey's saloon wan starry July
avenin' an' staggered into his familyar seat, holdin'
in his hand a bit iv soiled paper which he tore into
fragmints an' hurled into th' coal scuttle.   On that
crumpled parchmint findin' a sombre grave among th'
disinterred relics iv an age long past, to wit, th' cari-
boniferious or coal age, was written th' iver-mim'rable
pome:   " Ode to Gin."   Our frind had scribbled it
hastily at th' dinner iv th' Betther-thin-Shakespere
Club, an' had attimpted to read it to his wife through
th' keyhole iv her bedroom dure an' met no response
fr'm th' fillystein but a pitcher iv wather through th'
thransom.   Forchnitly he had presarved a copy on
his cuff an' th' gem was not lost to posterity.   But
such was th' home life iv wan iv th' gr-reatest iv lithry
masters, a man indowed be nachure with all that shud
make a woman adore him as is proved be his tindher

varses: ' To Carrie,' ' To Maude,' ' To Flossie,' ' To Angebel,' ' To Queenie,' an' so foorth. De Bonipoort in his cillybrated ' Mimores,' in which he tells ivrything unpleasant he see or heerd in his frinds' houses, gives a sthrikin' pitcher iv a scene that happened befure his eyes. ' Afther a few basins iv absceenthe in th' reev gosh,' says he, ' Parnassy invited us home to dinner. Sivral iv th' bum vivonts was hard to wake up, but fin'lly we arrived at th' handsome cellar where our gr-reat frind had installed his unworthy fam'ly. Ivrything pinted to th' admirable taste iv th' thrue artist. Th' tub, th' washboard, th' biler singin' on th' fire, th' neighbor's washin' dancin' on the clothes rack, were all in keepin' with th' best ideels iv what a pote's home shud be. Th' wife, a faded but still pretty woman, welcomed us more or less, an' with th' assistance iv sivral bottles iv paint we had brought with us, we was soon launched on a feast iv raison an' a flow iv soul. Unhappily befure th' raypast was con-cluded a mis'rable scene took place. Amid cries iv approval, Parnassy read his mim'rable pome intitled: ' I wisht I nivir got marrid.' Afther finishin' in a perfect roar of applause, he happened to look up an' see his wife callously rockin' th' baby. With th' impetchosity so charackteristic iv th' man, he broke a soup plate over her head an' burst into tears on th' flure, where gentle sleep soon soothed th' pangs iv a weary heart. We left as quitely as we cud, considherin' th' way th' chairs was placed, an' wanst undher th' stars comminted on th' ir'ny iv fate that condimned so great a man to so milancholy a distiny."

" ' This,' says our author, ' was th' daily life iv th' hayro f'r tin years. In what purgatory will that infamous woman suffer if Hiven thinks as much iv janiuses as we think iv oursilves. Forchnitly th' pote was soon to be marcifully relieved. He left her an' she marrid a boorjawce with whom she led a life iv coarse happiness. It is sad to relate that some years aftherward th' great pote, havin' called to make a short touch on th' woman f'r whom he had sacryficed so much, was unfeelingly kicked out iv th' boorjawce's plumbin' shop.'

" So, ye see, Hinnissy, why a woman oughtn't to marry a janius. She can't be cross or peevish or angry or jealous or frivolous or annything else a woman ought to be at times f'r fear it will get into th' ditchn'ry iv bio-graphy, an' she'll go down to histhry as a termygant. A termygant, Hinnissy, is a woman who's heerd talkin' to her husband after they've been marrid a year. Hogan says all janiuses was unhappily marrid. I guess that's thrue iv their wives, too. He says if ye hear iv a pote who got on with his fam'ly, scratch him fr'm ye'er public lib'ry list. An' there ye ar-re."

" Ye know a lot about marredge," said Mr. Hennessy.

" I do," said Mr. Dooley.

" Ye was niver marrid? "

" No," said Mr. Dooley. " No, I say, givin' three cheers. I know about marredge th' way an asthronomer knows about th' stars. I'm studyin' it through me glass all th' time."

" Ye're an asthronomer," said Mr. Hennessy;
" but," he added, tapping himself lightly on the chest,
" I'm a star."

" Go home," said Mr. Dooley crossly, " befure th'
mornin' comes to put ye out."

# Reform Administration

" **W**HY is it," asked Mr. Hennessy, " that a rayform administhration always goes to th' bad? "

" I'll tell ye," said Mr. Dooley. " I tell ye ivrything an' I'll tell ye this. In th' first place 'tis a gr-reat mistake to think that annywan ra-aly wants to rayform. Ye niver heerd iv a man rayformin' himsilf. He'll rayform other people gladly. He likes to do it. But a healthy man'll niver rayform while he has th' strenth. A man doesn't rayform till his will has been impaired so he hasn't power to resist what th' pa-apers calls th' blandishments iv th' timpter. An' that's thruer in politics thin annywhere else.

" But a rayformer don't see it. A rayformer thinks he was ilicted because he was a rayformer, whin th' thruth iv th' matther is he was ilicted because no wan knew him. Ye can always ilict a man in this counthry on that platform. If I was runnin' f'r office, I'd change me name, an' have printed on me cards: ' Give him a chanst; he can't be worse.' He's ilicted because th' people don't know him an' do know th' other la-ad; because Mrs. Casey's oldest boy was clubbed be a polisman, because we cudden't get wather above th' third story wan day, because th' sthreet car didn't stop f'r us, because th' Flannigans bought a pianny, because we was near run over be a mail wagon, because th' saloons are open Sundah night, because they're not open all day, an' because we're tired seein' th' same face at th' window whin we go down to pay th' wather taxes. Th' rayformer don't know this. He thinks you an' me, Hinnissy, has been watchin' his spotless career f'r twenty years, that we've read all he had to say on th' evils iv pop'lar sufferage befure th' Society f'r the Bewildermint iv th' Poor, an' that we're achin' in ivry joint to have him dhrag us be th' hair iv th' head fr'm th' flowin' bowl an' th' short card game, make good citizens iv us an' sind us to th' pinitinchry. So th' minyit he gets into th' job he begins a furyous attimpt to convart us into what we've been thryin' not to be iver since we come into th' wurruld.

" In th' coorse iv th' twenty years that he spint attimptin' to get office, he managed to poke a few warrum laws conthrollin' th' pleasures iv th' poor into th' stachoo book, because no wan cared about thim or because they made business betther f'r th' polis, an' whin he's in office, he calls up th' Cap'n iv the polis an' says he: ' If these laws ar-re bad laws th' way to end thim is to enfoorce thim.' Somebody told him that, Hinnissy. It isn't thrue, d'ye mind. I don't care who said it, not if 'twas Willum Shakespere. It isn't thrue. Laws ar-re made to throuble people an' th' more throuble they make th' longer they stay on th' stachoo book. But th' polis don't ast anny questions. Says they: ' They'll be less money in th' job but we need some recreation,' an' that night a big copper comes down th' sthreet, sees me settin' out on th' front stoop with me countenance dhraped with a tin pail,

fans me with his club an' runs me in. Th' woman nex'
dure is locked up f'r sthringin' a clothes line on th'
roof, Hannigan's boy Tim gets tin days f'r keepin' a
goat, th' polis resarves are called out to protict th'
vested rights iv property against th' haynyous push-
cart man, th' stations is crowded with felons charged
with maintainin' a hose conthrary to th' stachoos made
an' provided, an' th' tindherline is all over town. A
rayformer don't think annything has been accom-
plished if they'se a vacant bedroom in th' pinitinchry.
His motto is ' Arrest that man.'

" Whin a rayformer is ilicted he promises ye a business administhration. Some people want that but I
don't. Th' American business man is too fly. He's all
right, d'ye mind. I don't say annything again' him.
He is what Hogan calls th' boolwarks iv pro-gress, an'
we cudden't get on without him even if his scales are a
little too quick on th' dhrop. But he ought to be left
to dale with his akels. 'Tis a shame to give him a
place where he can put th' comether on millions iv people that has had no business thrainin' beyond occasionally handin' a piece iv debased money to a car
conductor on a cold day. A reg'lar pollytician can't
give away an alley without blushin', but a business
man who is in pollytics jus' to see that th' civil sarvice
law gets thurly enfoorced, will give Lincoln Park an'
th' public libr'y to th' beef thrust, charge an admission
price to th' lake front an' make it a felony f'r annywan
to buy stove polish outside iv his store, an' have it all
put down to public improvemints with a pitcher iv him
in th' corner stone.

" Fortchnitly, Hinnissy, a rayformer is seldom a business man. He thinks he is, but business men know diff'rent. They know what he is. He thinks business an' honesty is th' same thing. He does, indeed. He's got thim mixed because they dhress alike. His idee is that all he has to do to make a business administhration is to have honest men ar-round him. Wrong. I'm not sayin', mind ye, that a man can't do good work an' be honest at th' same time. But whin I'm hirin' a la-ad I find out first whether he is onto his job, an' after a few years I begin to suspect that he is honest, too. Manny a dishonest man can lay brick sthraight an' manny a man that wudden't steal ye'er spoons will break ye'er furniture. I don't want Father Kelly to hear me, but I'd rather have a competint man who wud steal if I give him a chanst, but I won't, do me plumbin' thin a person that wud scorn to help himsilf but didn't know how to wipe a joint. Ivry man ought to be honest to start with, but to give a man an office jus' because he's honest is like ilictin' him to Congress because he's a pathrite, because he don't bate his wife or because he always wears a right boot on th' right foot. A man ought to be honest to start with an' after that he ought to be crafty. A pollytician who's on'y honest is jus' th' same as bein' out in a winther storm without anny clothes on.

" Another thing about rayform administhrations is they always think th' on'y man that ought to hold a job is a lawyer. Th' raison is that in th' coorse iv his thrainin' a lawyer larns enough about ivrything to make a good front on anny subject to annybody who

[ 170 ]

doesn't know about it. So whin th' rayform administhration comes in th' mayor says: 'Who'll we make
chief iv polis in place iv th' misguided ruffyan who
has held th' job f'r twinty years?' 'Th' man f'r th'
place,' says th' mayor's adviser, 'is Arthur Lightout,'
he says. 'He's an ixcillent lawyer, Yale, '95, an'
is well up on polis matthers. Las' year he read a
paper on "The fine polis foorce iv London" befure
th' annyal meetin' iv th' S'ciety f'r Ladin' th'
Mulligan Fam'ly to a Betther an' Harder Life.
Besides,' he says, 'he's been in th' milishy an' th'
foorce needs a man who'll be afraid not to shoot in
case iv public disturbance.' So Arthur takes hold
iv th' constabulary an' in a year th' polis can all
read Emerson an' th' burglars begin puttin' up
laddhers an' block an' tackles befure eight A.M. An'
so it is on ivry side. A lawyer has charge iv the
city horse-shoein', another wan is clanin' th' sthreets,
th' author iv 'Gasamagoo on torts' is thryin' to dis-
pose iv th' ashes be throwin' thim in th' air on a
windy day, an' th' bright boy that took th' silver ware
f'r th' essay on *ne exeats* an' their relation to life is
plannin' a uniform that will be sarviceable an' con-
stitchoochinal f'r th' brave men that wurruks on th'
city dumps. An' wan day th' main rayformer goes
out expictin' to rayceive th' thanks iv th' community
an' th' public that has jus' got out iv jail f'r lettin' th'
wather run too long in th' bath tub rises up an' cries:
'Back to th' Univarsity Settlemint.' Th' man with
th' di'mon' in his shirt front comes home an' pushes th'
honest lawyers down th' steps, an' a dishonest horse

shoer shoes th' city's horses well, an' a crooked plumber
does th' city's plumbin' securely, an' a rascally polisman that may not be avarse to pickin' up a bet but
will always find out whin Pathrolman Scanlan slept
on his beat, takes hold iv th' polis foorce, an' we raysume our nachral condition iv illagal merrimint.   An'
th' rayformer spinds th' rest iv his life tellin' us where
we are wrong.   He's good at that.   On'y he don't
undherstand that people wud rather be wrong an'
comfortable thin right in jail."

" I don't like a rayformer," said Mr. Hennessy.

" Or anny other raypublican," said Mr. Dooley.

# Work and Sport

"A HARD time th' rich have injyin' life," said Mr. Dooley.

"I'd thrade with thim," said Mr. Hennessy.

"I wud not," said Mr. Dooley. "'Tis too much like hard wurruk. If I iver got hold iv a little mound iv th' money, divvle th' bit iv hardship wud I inflict on mesilf. I'd set on a large Turkish sofa an' have dancin' girls dancin' an' a mandolin orchesthree playin' to me. I wudden't move a step without bein' carrid. I'd go to bed with th' lark an' get up with th' night watchman. If annywan suggested physical exercise to me, I'd give him forty dollars to go away. I'd hire a prize fighter to do me fightin' f'r me, a pedesthreen to do me walkin', a jockey to do me ridin', an' a colledge pro-fissor to do me thinkin'. Here I'd set with a naygur fannin' me with osterich feathers, lookin' ca'mly out through me stained glass windies on th' rollin' mills, smokin' me good five cint seegar an' rejicin' to know how bad ye mus' be feelin' ivry time ye think iv me hoorded wealth.

"But that ain't th' way it comes out, Hinnissy. Higgins, the millyionaire, had th' same idee as me whin he was beginnin' to breed money with a dollar he ownded an' a dollar he took fr'm some wan that wasn't there at th' time. While he was hammerin' hoops on

a bar'l or dhrivin' pegs into a shoe, he'd stop wanst
in a while to wipe th' sweat off his brow whin th' boss
wasn't lookin' an' he'd say to himsilf : ' If I iver get
it, I'll have a man wheel me around on a chair.' But
as his stable grows an' he herds large dhroves down
to th' bank ivry week, he changes his mind, an' whin
he's got enough to injye life, as they say, he finds he's
up against it. His throubles has just begun. I know
in his heart Higgins' ideel iv luxury is enough buck-
wheat cakes an' a cozy corner in a Turkish bath, but
he can't injye it. He mus' be up an' doin'. An' th'
on'y things annywan around him is up an' doin' is
th' things he used to get paid f'r doin' whin he was a
young man.

" Arly in th' mornin' Higgins has got to be out exercisin' a horse to keep th' horse in good health. Higgins has no business on a horse an' he knows it. He
was built an' idycated f'r a cooper an' th' horse don't
fit him. Th' nachral way f'r Higgins to ride a horse
is to set well aft an' hang onto th' ears. But he's tol'
that's wrong an' he's made to set up sthraight an' be
a good fellow an' meet th' horse half way. An' if th'
horse don't run away with Higgins an' kill him, he's
tol' it's not a good horse an' he ought to sell it. An'
mind ye, he pays f'r that though he can't help raymimberin' th' man nex' dure fr'm him used to get tin
dollars a week f'r th' same job.

" Whin he was a young man, Higgins knowed a
fellow that dhruv four horses f'r a brewery. They
paid him well, but he hated his job. He used to come
in at night an' wish his parents had made him a

cooper, an' Higgins pitied him, knowin' he cudden't get out a life insurance policy an' his wife was scared to death all th' time. Now that Higgins has got th' money, he's took th' brewery man's job with worse horses an' him barred fr'm dhrivin' with more thin wan hand. An' does he get annything f'r it? On th' conth'ry, Hinnissy, it sets him back a large forchune. An' he says he's havin' a good time an' if th' brewery man come along an' felt sorry f'r him, Higgins wudden't exactly know why.

" Higgins has to sail a yacht raymimberin' how he despised th' Swede sailors that used to loaf in th' saloon near his house durin' th' winter; he has to run an autymobill, which is th' same thing as dhrivin' a throlley car on a windy day without pay; he has to play golf, which is th' same thing as bein' a letther-carryer without a dacint uniform; he has to play tennis, which is another wurrud f'r batin' a carpet; he has to race horses, which is the same thing as bein' a bookmaker with th' chances again' ye; he has to go abroad, which is th' same thing as bein' an immigrant; he has to set up late, which is th' same thing as bein' a dhrug clerk; an' he has to play cards with a man that knows how, which is th' same thing as bein' a sucker.

" He takes his good times hard, Hinnissy. A rich man at spoort is a kind iv non-union laborer. He don't get wages f'r it an' he don't dhrive as well as a milkman, ride as well as a stable-boy, shoot as well as a polisman, or autymobill as well as th' man that runs th' steam-roller. It's a tough life. They'se no rest f'r th' rich an' weary. We'll be readin' in th'

[ 177 ]

pa-apers wan iv these days: ' Alonzo Higgins, th' runner up in las' year's champeenship, showed gr-reat improvement in this year's brick layin' tournymint at Newport, an' won handily with about tin square feet to spare. He was nobly assisted be Regynald Van Stinyvant, who acted as his hod carryer an' displayed all th' agility which won him so much applause arlier in th' year.

" ' Th' Pickaways carrid off all th' honors in th' sewer-diggin' contest yesterdah, defatin'˙ th' Spadewells be five holes to wan. Th' shovel wurruk iv Cassidy th' banker was spicially noticeable. Th' colors iv th' Pickaways was red flannel undhershirts an' dark brown trousers.

" ' Raycreations iv rich men: Jawn W. Grates an' J. Pierpont Morgan ar-re to have a five days' shinglin' contest at Narragansett Pier. George Gold is thrainin' f'r th' autumn plumbin' jimkanny. Mitchigan avnoo is tore up fr'm Van Buren sthreet to th' belt line in priparation f'r th' contest in sthreet layin' between mimbers iv th' Assocyation iv More-Thin-Rich Spoorts. Th' sledge teams is completed but a few good tampers an' wather men is needed.'

" An' why not, Hinnissy? If 'tis fun to wurruk why not do some rale wurruk? If 'tis spoort to run an autymobill, why not run a locymotive? If dhrivin' a horse in a cart is a game, why not dhrive a delivery wagon an' carry things around? Sure, I s'pose th' raison a rich man can't undherstand why wages shud go higher is because th' rich can't see why annybody shud be paid f'r annything so amusin' as

wurruk. I bet ye Higgins is wondherin' at this moment why he was paid so much f'r puttin' rings
around a bar'l.

" No, sir, what's a rich man's raycreation is a poor
man's wurruk. Th' poor ar-re th' on'y people that
know how to injye wealth. Me idee iv settin' things
sthraight is to have th' rich who wurruk because they
like it, do th' wurruk f'r th' poor who wud rather rest.
I'll be happy th' day I see wan iv th' Hankerbilts
pushin' ye'er little go-cart up th' platform while ye
set in th' shade iv a three an' cheer him on his way.
I'm sure he'd do it if ye called it a spoort an' tol him
th' first man to th' dump wud be entitled to do it over
again against sthronger men nex' week. Wud ye
give him a tin cup that he cud put his name on?
Wud ye, Hinnissy? I'm sure ye wud."

" Why do they do it? " asked Mr. Hennessy.

" I dinnaw," said Mr. Dooley, " onless it is that th'
wan great object iv ivry man's life is to get tired
enough to sleep. Ivrything seems to be some kind iv
wurruk. Wurruk is wurruk if ye're paid to do it an'
it's pleasure if ye pay to be allowed to do it."

# The News of a Week

"**W**HAT'S goin' on this week in th' papers?" asked Mr. Hennessy.

"Ivrything," said Mr. Dooley. "It's been a turbylint week. I can hardly sleep iv nights thinkin' iv th' doin's iv people. Th' campinily at Venice has fallen down. 'Twas built in 1604 be th' Beezantiums an' raystored in 1402 be th' Dogs. It fell down because th' foundations was weak, because th' wind blew, because th' beautiful figure iv th' goolden angel on top iv it was fifteen feet high. It will be rebuilt or maybe not. Th' king iv Italy has given thirty-three billion liars to put it up again, an' siv'ral ladin' American archytects have offered to do th' job, makin' an office buildin' iv it. Th' campinily was wan iv th' proudest monymints iv Italy an' was used as a bell-tower at times, an' at other times as a gazabo where anny American cud take a peek at th' gran' canal an' compare it with th' Erie, th' Pannyma an' th' dhrainage iv the same name.

"Th' king iv England is bether. He's off in his yacht. So ar-re Laking, Treves, Smith, Barlow, Jones, Casey, Lister, thank Hiven! A hard life is science. Th' Hon'rable Joseph Choate is raycoverin' more slowly. He still sobs occas'nally in his sleep an' has ordhered all th' undher sicreties to have their vermyform appindixes raymoved as a token iv rayspict f'r th' sthricken nation. Th' Hon'rable Whitelaw Reid is havin' a cast iv his knee breeches made, which will be exhibited in New York durin' th' comin' winter.

" Me frind, J. Pierpont Morgan, has been takin' dinner with th' Impror Willum. It is undherstud he will presint him to th' Methropolytan Museem iv Art. There are said to be worse things there.

" Lord Salisberry has thrun up his job. Lord Salisberry was wan iv th' grandest an' mos' succissful statesmen iv modhren times. He niver did annything. He is succeeded be his nevvew, Misther Balfour, if I get th' name right, who has done less. It is expicted that Misther Balfour will have a good time. On rayceivin' th' congrathylations iv his colleague, Misther Chamberlain, he bought himsilf a rayvolver an' took out a policy on his life.

" A lady down east woke her husband up to tell him there was a burglar in th' house. Th' foolish woman. They'se always burglars in th' house. That's what burglars are f'r, an' houses. Instead iv argyin' th' pint in a loud voice, coughin' an' givin' th' burglar a chance to lave with dignity, this man got up an' was kilt. Now th' pa-apers with th' assistance iv th' officers iv th' law has discovered that th' lady took a boat ride with a gintleman frind in th' summer iv sixty-two, that she wanst quarreled with her husband about th' price iv a hat, that wan iv her lower teeth is plugged, that she wears a switch an' that she weeps whin she sees her childher. They'se a moral in this. It's ayether don't wake a man up out

iv a sound sleep, or don't get out iv bed till ye have to,
or don't bother a burglar whin ye see he's busy, or kill
th' iditor. I don't know which it is.

"Willum Jennings Bryan is readin' me frind
Grover Cleveland out iv th' party. He's usin' the
*Commoner* to read him out. That's a sure way.

"Mary McLane has been in town. I didn't see
her, me place not bein' a raysort f'r th' young an'
yearnin', an' especially me duckin' all lithry ladies iv
whativer sex. Mary McLane is th' author iv a book
called: 'Whin I am older I'll know betther.' Ye
ought to read it, Hinnissy.

"Th' Newport season is opened with gr-reat gayety an' th' aim iv rayturnin' husbands is much more
sure.

"Gin'ral Bragg fr'm up in Wisconsin has been
gettin' into throuble with our haughty allies, th' Cubians, he writin' home to his wife that ye might as
well thry to make a whistle out iv a pig's tail as a dacint man out iv a Cubian. Gin'ral Bragg will be
bounced an' he ought to be. He don't belong in
pollytics. His place is iditor iv a losin' newspaper.

"Gov'nor Taft has been in Rome showin' th'
wurruld how successful, sthraightforward, downright,
outspoken, manly, frank, fourteen ounces to th' pound
American business dalings can be again' th' worn-out
di-plomacy iv th' papal coort. Whin last heerd fr'm
this astoot an' able man, backed up be th' advice iv
Elihoo Root iv York state, was makin' his way
tow'rd Manila on foot, an' siv'ral mimbers iv th'
colledge iv cardinals was heerd to regret that Ameri-

can statesmen were so thin they cudden't find anything to fit thim in his thrunk.

"Cholera is ragin' in th' Ph'lippeens vice Gin'ral
Jake Smith, raymoved.

"Th' stock market is boomin' an' business has become so dull elsewhere that some iv th' best known
outside operators ar-re obliged to increase th' depth
iv th' goold coatin' on th' brick to nearly an inch.

"Th' capital iv th' nation has raymoved to Eyes-
ther Bay, a city on th' north shore iv Long Island,
with a popylation iv three millyion clams, an' a number iv mosquitos with pianola attachments an' steel
rams. There day be day th' head iv th' nation thran-
sacts th' nation's business as follows: four A.M., a
plunge into th' salt, salt sea an' a swim iv twenty
miles; five A.M., horse-back ride, th' prisidint insthructin' his two sons, aged two and four rayspic-
tively, to jump th' first Methodist church without
knockin' off th' shingles; six A.M., wrestles with a
thrained grizzly bear; sivin A.M., breakfast; eight
A.M., Indyan clubs; nine A.M., boxes with Sharkey;
tin A.M., bates th' tinnis champeen; iliven A.M., ray-
ceives a band iv rough riders an' person'lly super-
vises th' sindin' iv th' ambylance to look afther th' injured in th' village; noon, dinner with Sharkey,
Oscar Featherstone, th' champeen roller-skater iv
Harvard, '98, Pro-fissor McGlue, th' archyologist,
Lord Dum de Dum, Mike Kehoe, Immanuel Kant
Gumbo, th' naygro pote, Horrible Hank, t' bad lands
scout, Sinitor Lodge, Lucy Emerson Tick, th' writer
on female sufferage, Mud-in-the-Eye, th' chief iv th'

## The News of a Week

Ogallas, Gin'ral Powell Clayton, th' Mexican mine expert, four rough riders with their spurs on, th' Am-bassadure iv France an' th' Cinquovasti fam'ly, jugglers. Th' conversation, we larn fr'm wan iv th' guests who's our spoortin' iditor, was jined in be th' prisidint an' dealt with art, boxin', lithrachoor, horsebreakin', science, shootin', pollytics, how to kill a mountain line, di-plomacy, lobbing, pothry, th' pivot blow, rayform, an' th' campaign in Cubia. Whin our rayporther was dhriven off th' premises be wan iv th' rough riders, th' head iv th' nation was tachin' Lord Dum de Dum an' Sicrety Hay how to do a hand-spring, an' th' other guests was scattered about th' lawn, boxin', rasslin', swingin' on th' thrapeze, ridin' th' buckin' bronco an' shootin' at th' naygro pote f'r th' dhrinks—in short enjyin' an ideel day in th' count'ry.

" An' that's all th' news," said Mr. Dooley. " There ye ar-re jus' as if ye cud read. That's all that's happened. Ain't I a good newspaper? Not a dull line in me. Sind in ye'er small ads."

" Sure, all that's no news," said Mr. Hennessy, discontentedly. " Hasn't there annything happened? Hasn't anny wan been—been kilt? "

" There ye ar-re," said Mr. Dooley. " Be news ye mane misfortune. I suppose near ivry wan does. What's wan man's news is another man's throubles. In these hot days, I'd like to see a pa-aper with naw-thin' in it but affectionate wives an' loyal husbands an' prosp'rous, smilin' people an' money in th' bank an' three a day. That's what I'm lookin' f'r in th' hot weather."

## Observations by Mr. Dooley

" Th' newspapers have got to print what happens,"
said Mr. Hennessy.

" No," said Mr. Dooley, " they've got to print
what's diff'rent.   Whiniver they begin to put head-
lines on happiness, contint, varchoo, an' charity, I'll
know things is goin' as wrong with this counthry as I
think they ar-re ivry naytional campaign."

# The End of the War

# THE END OF THE WAR

"WHY did th' Boers quit fightin'?" asked Mr. Hennessy.

"Th' supply iv British gin'rals give out," said Mr. Dooley. "They were fin'lly crushed be th' surrindher iv Gin'ral Lord Mechoon.

"Up to that time th' British had niver gained anny important advantage. They'd surrindhered ninety or a hundherd thousan' private sojery, thirty or forty colonels, near all th' officers iv th' guards, th' Northumberland Fusileers over an' over again, an' Winston Churchill; they'd hurled gr-reat masses iv th' Impeeryal Yeomanry into th' prison camps iv th' Boers; they'd surrindhered rifles, an' ammunition an' pompons an' mules, but nary a British gin'ral among thim. Although a smaller foorce, Hinnissy, th' Boers had th' advantage iv knowin' ivry foot iv th' ground they were fightin' on. Manny iv thim had just gone there, while th' British had been on th' ground f'r three years with an opporchunity to f'rget something ivry hour. Th' crafty Dutch, marchin' almost as well be bright moonlight as in th' day time, proceedin' without rest f'r hours at a time, always placin' th' catridge in th' gun befure firin', hardy, vigorous an' accustomed to th' veldt, had eluded all attempts to hand thim th' roast beef iv Merry England in th' shape iv a gin'ral.

" But whin Gin'ral, me Lord Kitchener, th' Great
Coon Conqueror, wint to South Africa, like th' stern
an' remorseless warryor that he is, he detarmined to
niver rest till he had desthroyed th' inimy. In less
thin two years, he had evolved his sthrategy. I will
tell ye what it was, because ye're inthrested in military plans. He spread his magnificent army iv gallant Britons out in a long line that sthretched clane
acrost th' counthry, wan yeoman deep. Thin, ac-
companied be his sub-gin'rals, he moved out in th'
followin' ordher. I'll dhraw it f'r ye, as I see it in
th' pa-aper. Here ye ar-re:

" The band,

" Gin'ral Lord Kitchener, K.C.B., K.N., K.L.K.
G.K.R. (with medals),

" The other gin'rals,

" Pianos, Pianolas, Cottage Organs, Ping Pong
Sets, Tennis Bats, Bridge Scores, Cricket Stumps,
War Corryspondints,

" Th' Avingin' Line,

" Their horses,

" Their ammunition,

" Their Food, and

" Their Rifles.

" As th' dhread formation moved off in th' bright
sunlight iv that fair day in March, with th' band
playin' a quick shtep an' th' colors flyin' in th' air,
it was a sight to make ivry Englishman proud iv th'
fact that he had to be an Englishman. Detarmination was written in ivry face—th' detarmination to
go on at anny risk till tea time. No flinchin', no

hisitation, ivry man with his head erect an' th' feelin'
in his heart that on him rested th' security iv th'
impire if so. On, an' iver on they marched, fr'm
Spimfontein, past th' gleamin' spires iv Wa-aber-
neck, till they saw in th' distance th' long, low line
iv purple light that marked th' walls iv Boobenas-
tofein. It was thin four o'clock P.M., an' th' column
halted while th' bugles blew th' cheery call to tea.
Eager hands unshipped th' marmalade an' opened
th' caddies, bread was toasted on th' small stoves
carrid be ivry officer's valet, th' pickets an' scouts
were dispatched f'r plum cake an' f'rgettin' f'r a
moment th' thriles iv th' campaign, th' rough warryors indulged in that repast that has done so much
to make Englishmen what they are. At siven, havin'
taken all precautions, havin' placed th' powdher in
a cool runnin' brook an' tethered th' mules to th'
rifles, th' vast army slept. It was breakfast time
whin th' God iv Slumber was dhriven off be th' other
British God iv Appetite. Such, Hinnissy, is th'
brief story iv Gin'ral Kitchener's cillybrated dhrive,
as I read it in th' pa-apers.

" To some extint it was successful an' to some other
extints not. Th' bands were good. Th' tea was fine,
though some prefer Oolong. Rifles, pompons, mules,
fusileers, etcethry had been lost. But not wan British
gin'ral had been captured. Not wan. They were all
at breakfast an' th' great heart iv th' British nation
was sad. Th' great heart begun to grumble, which
is a way th' great heart iv a nation has. It ast what
was th' use iv this costly manoover—if they was as

manny gin'rals left afther it as befure. While in
this mood, it was ilicthryfied be a piece iv startlin'
intilligince. Th' whisper ran round, grew to be a
murmur, increased to a roar, mounted to a shriek that
Mechoon was captured.

"It seemed too good to be thrue. No wan cud
believe it at first. But fin'lly it was officially announced in Parlymint be that hot headed ol' pathrite,
Lord Salsberry himsilf. In a voice choked be emotion
he arose an' give three cheers. Afther which he read
Gin'ral Kitchener's dispatch: ' I have th' pleasure
to rayport that yisterdah at nine o'clock Lord
Mechoon be a superb sthrategy had himsilf surrounded be an infeeryor foorce iv Boers undher Gin-
'ral Delaney or some such name. Our cust'mary
precaution iv dhrawin' in th' pickets afther night-
fall an' buryin' our rifles, which had repeatedly failed
in th' past owin' to th' caution iv th' Boers, wurruked
admirably. Gin'ral Delaney was completely taken
be surprise an' befure he cud recover, Lord Mechoon
had thrown himsilf around his neck an' given him
his cigreet case in token iv submission. Th' com-
mand behaved with gr-reat gallantry. In wan case,
a whole comp'ny surrindhered to wan Boer. I am
sindin' ricommindations f'r th' Victorya cross be
freight. Unforchunitly our casulties were very heavy.
Mesilf an' nearly all th' other gin'rals escaped capture. But betther luck nex' time. Gin'ral Dewet
is about a mile fr'm here, if in Africa at all, or indeed, livin'. Gin'ral Botha is said to be in Ioway,
though ye can't believe ivrything ye see in th'

pa-apers. Wan or th' other may be enthrapped into kidnapin' me. In th' manetime I am plannin' right along. I sleep constantly in clothes becomin' me station, an' th' impire may rely on me not makin' a show iv mesilf whin I am took. Ye'ers hopefully, Kitchener.'

" Th' Boers niver raycovered fr'm th' tur'ble blow. Their spirits was crushed. Their hopes had fled. Th' kindergartens had opened an' manny iv their bravest warryors had been carried off be their mothers. Anny moment they might be surrounded an' surrin- dhered to. So wan mornin' th' entire mighty army, th' whole thirty-two iv them, histed th' white flag an' presinted their bill."

" An' so th' war is over? " asked Mr. Hennessy.

" On'y part iv it," said Mr. Dooley. " Th' part that ye see in th' pitcher pa-apers is over, but th' tax collector will continyoo his part iv th' war with re- lentless fury. Cav'lry charges are not th' on'y wars in a rale war."

Newport

# NEWPORT

"ABOUT this time ivry year," said Mr. Dooley, "I go to Newport f'r th' summer."

"Ye go where?" asked Mr. Hennessy.

"I go to Newport," said Mr. Dooley, calmly, "in th' pa-apers. Newport's always there. I may not find annything about th' fire at th' yards or th' war in th' Ph'lippeens, but if Mrs. Rasther opens a can iv salmon or pounds th' top off an egg, it's down in black an' white be th' fearless hands iv th' iditor. 'Tis a gr-reat joy bein' lithry an' knowin' how to read. Th' air is hot in Ar-rchey Road; ye can see it. It looks an' feels like hot soup with people floatin' around in it like viggytables. Th' smoke poors fr'm th' chimbly iv th' rollin' mills an' comes right down on th' sthreet an' jines us. People ar-re lyin' out iv doors with their mouths open. They'se a gr-reat dale iv cholery infantum an' a few deleeryam thremens. If I cudden't read I'd be hot about th' weather an' things. But whin th' day is darkest an' I don't want to see me best cukkin' frind, I takes me yacht at th' top iv page eight an' goes sailin' off to Newport in me shirt sleeves with twelve inches iv malt in th' hook iv me thumb, an' there I stay till I want to come back an' rest.

"'Th' autymobill season has opened in deadly earnest. Manny new machines is seen daily an' wan

iv th' delights iv th' summer colony is to go out iv
an avenin' an' see th' farmers iv th' neighborhood
pluckin' their horses fr'm th' top branches iv threes.
Th' younger Hankerbilt has atthracted much attintion be his acc'rate ridin'. Th' other day he made
a scoor iv eight fr'm a runnin' start in tin minyits
an' this in spite iv th' fact that he was obliged to
come back to th' last wan, a Swede named Olson, an'
bump him over again.

" ' Misther Graball, th' Muskegon millionaire who
got into s'ciety las' year be dyin' his hair green an'
givin' a dinner at which all th' guests rayceived a
lumber mill as sooveneers, has returned suddenly fr'm
th' West an' his house party is over.

" ' Little Aigrette Vandycooker has a tooth, her
elder sister a markess, an' her mother a siparation.

" ' Misther an' Mrs. Roger Smitherson an' frind
ar-re spindin' th' summer at frind's house.'

" Gin'rally we lade a life iv quite an' iligant luxury. Wud ye like a line on me daily routine? Well,
in th' mornin' a little spin in me fifty-horse power
' Suffer-little-childher,' in th' afthernoon a whirl
over th' green wathers iv th' bay in me goold-
an'-ivory yacht, in th' avenin' dinner with a monkey
or something akelly as good, at night a few leads
out iv th' wrong hand, some hasty wurruds an' so
to bed. Such is th' spoortin' life in Rhode Island,
th' home iv Roger Williams an' others not so
much. It grows tiresome afther awhile. I confess
to ye, Algernon Hinnissy, that befure th' monkey
was inthrajooced, I was sufferin' fr'm what Hogan

calls onwee, which is th' same thing as ingrowin'
money. I had got tired iv puttin' new storeys
on me cottage an' ridin' up in th' ilivator fr'm th'
settin' room on th' eighth flure to th' dinin' room on
th' twinty-ninth, I didn't care about ayether thrap-
shootin' or autymobillin', I felt like givin' a cawrnation dinner to th' poor iv th' village an' feedin' thim
me polo ponies, I didn't care whether th' champagne
bar'ls was kept iced, whether th' yacht was as long
as th' wan ownded be th' Ginger Snap king nex' dure,
whether I had three or tin millyon dollars in me
pants pocket in th' mornin' or whether th' Poles in
th' coal mine was sthrikin' f'r wan dollar an' forty-
siven or wan dollar an' forty-eight cints a day. I
was tired iv ivrything. Life had me be th' throat,
th' black dog was on me back. I felt like suicide or
wurruk. Thin come th' bright idee iv me young
frind an' th' monkey saved me. He give me something to live f'r. Perhaps we too may be monkeys
some day an' be amusin'. We don't talk half as loud
or look half as foolish or get dhrunk half as quick,
but give us a chanst. We're a young people an'
th' monkeys is an old, old race. They've been New-
portin' f'r cinchries. Sure that ol' la-ad who said
man was descinded fr'm monkeys knew what he was
talkin' about. Descinded, but how far?

"Now, don't go gettin' cross about th' rich, Hinnissy. Put up that dinnymite. Don't excite ye'ersilf
about us folks in Newport. It's always been th' same
way, Father Kelly tells me. Says he: ' If a man is
wise, he gets rich an' if he gets rich, he gets foolish,

or his wife does. That's what keeps th' money movin' around. What comes in at th' ticker goes out at th' wine agent. F'river an' iver people have been growin' rich, goin' down to some kind iv a Newport, makin' monkeys iv thimsilves an' goin' back to th' jungle. 'Tis a steady pro-cission. Aisy come, lazy go. In ivry little hamlet in this broad land, there's some man with a broad jaw an' th' encouragement iv a good woman, makin' ready to shove some other man off his steam yacht. At this very minyit whin I speak, me frind Jawn Grates has his eye on Hankerbilk's house. He wud swing a hammock in th' woodshed this year, but nex' he may have his feet up on th' bannister iv th' front stoop. Whin a captain iv industhry stops dhrinkin' at th' bar, he's near his finish. If he ain't caught in his own person, th' constable will get to his fam'ly. Ye read about th' union iv two gr-reat fortunes. A dollar meets another dollar, they are conganial, have sim'lar tastes, an' manny mutual frinds. They are marrid an' bring up a fam'ly iv pennies, dimes, thirty-cintses an' countherfeits. An' afther awhile, th' fam'ly passes out iv circylation. That's th' histhry iv it,' says Father Kelly. ' An',' says he, ' I'm glad there is a Newport,' he says. ' It's th' exhaust pipe,' he says. ' Without it we might blow up,' he says. ' It's th' hole in th' top iv th' kettle,' he says. ' I wish it was bigger,' he says."

" Oh, well," said Mr. Hennessy, " we are as th' Lord made us."

" No," said Mr. Dooley, " lave us be fair. Lave us take some iv th' blame oursilves."

# Arctic  Exploration

"THIS here business iv Artic exploration's th' gran' pursoot," said Mr. Dooley. "A gran', comfortable, fightin', quarrelin' business."

"What's it all about?" asked Mr. Hennessy. "Why shud annywan want to go to th' North Pole? Ain't it cold enough here?"

"I niver cud quite make it out," said Mr. Dooley. "I've heerd tell that years ago, befure th' fire or th' war, some wan had an idee in his foolish head that they was a gran' sea up there with blue wather dimplin' in th' moonlight an' cocynut threes growin' on th' shore an' if a man cud on'y get in with his boat, he cud sail around th' wurruld an' fetch up in Chiny. That idee blew up an' thin some wan said 'twud be a fine thing f'r science if a white man cud get to th' North Pole. What he'd do if he got there no wan has anny thought. Accordin' to what I hear, th' North Pole ain't like a tillygraft pole, a barber pole, a fishin' pole, a clothes pole, a poll-tax, a Maypole, a Russhyan Pole, or annything that ye can see, smell or ate. Whin ye get to it, it is no diff'rent fr'm bein' annywhere on th' ice. Th' on'y way ye know ye're there is be consultin' a pocket arithmetic, a watch an' a compass. Don't get it into ye'er head that if me frind Baldwin or Peary iver wint north iv Milwaukee an' come acrost th' North Pole they'd carve their names on it or hist a flag over it or bring it home with thim on a thruck an' set it up on th' lake front. Th' north pole is a gigantic column iv cold air, some says hot, an' an enthusyastic explorer that wasn't lookin' where he wint might pass right through it without knowin'.

" In th' arly days whin an explorer wint off to find th' Pole, he bought himsilf a sheepskin coat, a couple iv dogs, a pair iv skates, an' a bottle iv pickled onions an' set out bravely, an' th' people watched th' fam'ly to see what other form th' lunacy wud take. Afther awhile he ayether come back or he didn't. Sometimes th' Esqueemo lady didn't care to lave her pleasant home in th' land iv perpetchool blubber an' in that case th' hardy mariner remained in th' frozen north. I niver cud see th' advantages iv life in th' Artic regions. 'Tis thrue th' nights is six months long an' sleep is wan iv th' spoorts that age hasn't deprived me iv. It mus' be a gr-reat counthry f'r burglars. But f'r a plain wurrukin' man it's very thryin'. Think iv a six months' wurrukin' day. Ye get ye'er breakfast at sun-up in March an' ye don't set down to dinner till th' first iv June. Thin comes a long afthernoon an' I tell ye whin th' whistle blows at six o'clock October, it's a welcome sound it sinds to ye'er ears. Ye go home an' all th' childher has growed up an' th' news in th' mornin' pa-per is six months' old. Ye lie around readin' an' playin' cards f'r a month or two an' thin ye yawn an' set th' alarm clock f'r March an' says: ' Mah, it's th' fifteenth iv

Novimber an' time th' childher was abed,' an' go to sleep. About Christmas th' good woman wakes ye up to look f'r th' burglar an' afther ye've paddled around in th' ice floe f'r a week, ye climb back into bed grumblin' an' go to sleep again. Afther awhile ye snore an' th' wife iv ye'er bosom punches ye. ' What time is it? ' says ye. ' It's a quarther past th' fifteenth iv Janooary,' says she, ' an' that siren iv ye'ers has been goin' since New Year's day.' At March ye ar-re aroused be th' alarm clock an' ye go out to feed th' seals an' I tell ye, ye need a shave. It mus' be a quare sinsation to wake up in th' mornin' an' find that th' kid ye tucked into bed th' night be-fure has grown side-whiskers in his sleep an' his feet has pushed out th' foot iv th' cradle. Not f'r my money, Hinnissy. Th' Artic regions f'r thim that likes thim but give me a land where ye don't tell th' time iv day be th' almynac.

" But other people is diff'rent. Th' boldest Artic explorer is a man that's made his money out iv sellin' base-burnin' stoves an' has chillblains in July. Such a man is niver continted till he's started somebody off f'r th' northest north. An' he has no throuble to find a man. Nex' to bein' invited on a private yacht to sail in th' Middyteranyan, th' nicest thing a millyonaire can do f'r ye is to make an Artic explorer iv ye. Th' prelim'naries is great spoort. F'r two years ye go round th' counthry letchrin' on ' What I will see in th' Artic regions whin I get there if at all.' Fin'lly ye set off with th' fleet, consistin' iv a ship f'r ye'ersilf, three f'r th' provisions, two f'r th'

clothes an' wan f'r th' diaries. They'se also a convoy. Th' business iv th' convoy is to dhrop in at
Thromsoe in Norway an' ast f'r news iv ye. Thromsoe is wan iv th' farthest north places that anny explorer has been. But it well repays a visit, bein' a
thrivin', bustlin' Swede city with a good club. Afther
th' long sthruggle with th' pitiliss ice machine it is
very pleasant to dhrop in on this hospital community
an' come back that night be thrain. Well, as I was
sayin', wan explorer starts off in a fur suit an' has
th' time iv his life an' th' other explorer stays at
home an' suffers th' crool hardships an' bitther dis-
app'intments iv life in Brooklyn. Lashed to his
rockin' chair, he shivers ivry time th' wind blows an'
he thinks iv his hardy partner facin' th' purls iv that
far-off region iv ice an' snow an' funny little Esqueemo women in union garments iv fur. ' He's in
Greenland now; he's battlin' with th' deadly ice floe;
now he's rasslin' with a Polar bear; he's up; he's
away; he's reached th' Pole; he's pullin' it up be th'
roots; bravo Baldy!' An' so he goes till his hands
is all chapped fr'm thinkin' iv th' cold an' his leg
is lame fr'm th' encounther with a Polar bear an' his
rockin' chair is in danger iv bein' dashed to pieces
again' th' threacherous pianny. An' wan day a
message comes fr'm th' other explorer: ' Rio Janeiro.
We have rayturned, baffled but not defeated. Th'
pickled walnuts give out befure we reached th' West
Indies. As far as we've gone we've had excellent
raysults. Th' cap'n, th' mate, th' cook, th' stewart
an' eighty per cint iv th' crew is in ir'ns an' as soon

as I've got this tillygram off I'm goin' in to punch th' surgeon. I congratylate ye. Ye'er name will stand high among th' binnyfactors iv science. We have demonsthrated beyond fear iv conthrydiction that th' gulf sthream is jus' where it was an' that volcanoes ain't what they are cracked up to be. Our motto is: " Niver give up th' ship. It's too comfortable." Who's ye'er banker here?' Whin th' millyionaire dies iv exposure, a victim to science, th' mariner rayturns an' letchers on th' subject: ' Quarrels I have had in th' frozen north.' Talk about th' terrors iv Artic exploration, Hinnissy! There's where ye get thim. Did ye iver go to an Artic exploration letcher? I did wanst. They was wan down at th' brothers' school las' winther. I've been lame iver since.

" None iv it in mine, if ye plaze. It's too hot wurruk in thim clothes. An' aven if ye get up near th' pole, what's it good f'r? Th' climate is disagreeable, an' th' s'ciety is monotonous. Ivrybody dhresses alike. Th' wan tailor makes th' clothes f'r pah, mah, Lucille an' th' Polar bear out iv th' same patthern. If ye go to coort a girl, ye don't know befure she speaks whether 'tis hersilf or her Uncle Mike. I heerd iv an Artic explorer wanst that held hands with a Swede sicond mate f'r over an hour befure he ralized his mistake.

" No, sir, no Artic explorations f'r me, ayether pers'nally or be check. But if I did go into it, I know who I'd sind. I'd not fool around with people who begin to cough within sight iv th' car barns. I'd utilize th' folks in th' neighborhood. I'd pathronize home industhries. Th' Pole f'r th' polars, says I. They mus' be hundherds iv la-ads up in that part iv th' wurruld that'd be willin' to earn an honest dollar be discoverin' th' pole. With thim 'twud be like ye goin' down to explore th' stock yards. I bet manny iv thim knows th' pole as well as I know Haley's slough. Ye'd prob'ly find they've hung their washin' on it f'r years an' manny iv th' kids has shinned up it."

" Who'd ye sind? " asked Mr. Hennessy.

" Esqueemos," said Mr. Dooley.

# Machinery

MR. DOOLEY was reading from a paper. " 'We live,' he says, ' in an age iv won-dhers. Niver befure in th' histhry iv th' wurruld has such pro-gress been made.'

" Thrue wurruds an' often spoken. Even in me time things has changed. Whin I was a la-ad Long Jawn Wintworth cud lean his elbows on th' highest buildin' in this town. It took two months to come here fr'm Pittsburg on a limited raft an' a stage coach that run fr'm La Salle to Mrs. Murphy's hotel. They wasn't anny tillygraft that I can raymimber an' th' sthreet car was pulled be a mule an' dhruv be an engineer be th' name iv Mulligan. We thought we was a pro-grissive people. Ye bet we did. But look at us today. I go be Casey's house tonight an' there it is a fine storey-an'-a-half frame house with Casey settin' on th' dure shtep dhrinkin' out iv a pail. I go be Casey's house to-morrah an' it's a hole in th' groun'. I rayturn to Casey's house on Thursdah an' it's a fifty-eight storey buildin' with a morgedge onto it an' they're thinkin' iv takin' it down an' re-placin' it with a modhren sthructure. Th' shoes that Corrigan th' cobbler wanst wurruked on f'r a week, hammerin' away like a woodpecker, is now tossed out be th' dozens fr'm th' mouth iv a masheen. A cow goes lowin' softly in to Armours an' comes out glue,

beef, gelatine, fertylizer, celooloid, joolry, sofy
cushions, hair restorer, washin' sody, soap, lithrachoor an' bed springs so quick that while aft she's
still cow, for'ard she may be annything fr'm buttons
to Pannyma hats. I can go fr'm Chicago to New
York in twinty hours, but I don't have to, thank th'
Lord. Thirty years ago we thought 'twas marvelous
to be able to tillygraft a man in Saint Joe an' get
an answer that night. Now, be wireless tillygraft
ye can get an answer befure ye sind th' tillygram if
they ain't careful. Me friend Macroni has done that.
Be manes iv his wondher iv science a man on a ship
in mid-ocean can sind a tillygram to a man on shore,
if he has a confid'rate on board. That's all he needs.
Be mechanical science an' thrust in th' op'rator annywan can set on th' shore iv Noofoundland an' chat
with a frind in th' County Kerry.

"Yes, sir, mechanical science has made gr-reat
sthrides. Whin I was a young man we used to think
Hor'ce Greeley was th' gr-reatest livin' American.
He was a gran' man, a gran' man with feathers beneath his chin an' specs on his nose like th' windows
in a diver's hemlet. His pollyticks an' mine cudden't
live in th' same neighborhood but he was a gran' man
all th' same. We used to take th' Cleveland Plain
Daler in thim days f'r raycreation an' th' New York
Thrybune f'r exercise. 'Twas considhered a test iv
a good natured dimmycrat if he cud read an article
in th' Thrybune without havin' to do th' stations iv
th' cross aftherward f'r what he said. I almost did
wanst but they was a line at th' end about a frind iv

mine be th' name iv Andhrew Jackson an' I wint out
an' broke up a Methodist prayer meetin'. He was th'
boy that cud put it to ye so that if ye voted th'
dimmycrat tickit it was jus' th' same as demandin'
a place in purgytory. Th' farmers wud plant annything fr'm a ruty baga to a congressman on his advice. He niver had money enough to buy a hat but
he cud go to th' sicrety iv th' threasury an' tell him
who's pitcher to put on th' useful valentines we thrade
f'r groceries.

"But if Hor'ce Greeley was alive today where'd he
be? Settin' on three inches iv th' edge iv a chair in
th' outside office iv me frind Pierpont Morgan waitin'
f'r his turn. In th' line is th' Imp'ror iv Germany,
th' new cook, th' prisidint iv a railroad, th' cap'n iv
th' yacht, Rimbrandt th' painther, Jawn W. Grates,
an' Hor'ce. Afther awhile th' boy at th' dure says:
'Ye're next, ol' party. Shtep lively f'r th' boss has
had a Weehawken Peerooginy sawed off on him this
mornin' an' he mustn't be kep' waitin'.' An' th'
iditor goes in. 'Who ar-re ye?' says th' gr-reat
man, givin' him wan iv thim piercin' looks that whin
a man gets it he has to be sewed up at wanst. 'I'm
ye'er iditor,' says Hor'ce. 'Which wan?' says Pierpont. 'Number two hundhred an' eight.' 'What's
ye'er spishilty?' 'Tahriff an' th' improvemint iv
th' wurruld,' says Hor'ce. 'See Perkins,' says Pierpont, an' th' intherview is over. Now what's made
th' change? Mechanical Science, Hinnissy. Some
wan made a masheen that puts steel billets within
th' reach iv all. Hince Charlie Schwab.

## Observations by Mr. Dooley

" What's it done f'r th' wurruld? says ye. It's done ivrything. It's give us fast ships an' an autymatic hist f'r th' hod, an' small flats an' a taste iv solder in th' peaches. If annybody says th' wurruld ain't betther off thin it was, tell him that a masheen has been invinted that makes honey out iv pethrolyum. If he asts ye why they ain't anny Shakesperes today, say: ' No, but we no longer make sausages be hand.'

" 'Tis pro-gress. We live in a cinchry iv pro-gress an' I thank th' Lord I've seen most iv it. Man an' boy I've lived pretty near through this wondherful age. If I was proud I cud say I seen more thin Julyus Cæsar iver see or cared to. An' here I am, I'll not say how old, still pushin' th' malt acrost th' counther at me thirsty counthrymen. All around me is th' refinemints iv mechanical janius. Instead iv broachin' th' beer kag with a club an' dhrawin' th' beer through a fassit as me Puritan forefathers done, I have that wondher iv invintive science th' beer pump. I cheat mesilf with a cash raygisther. I cut off th' end iv me good cigar with an injanyous device an' pull th' cork out iv a bottle with a conthrivance that wud've made that frind that Hogan boasts about, that ol' boy Archy Meeds, think they was witchcraft in th' house. Science has been a gr-reat blessin' to me. But amidst all these granjoors here am I th' same ol' antiquated combination iv bellows an' pump I always was. Not so good. Time has worn me out. Th' years like little boys with jackknives has carved their names in me top. Ivry day I have to write off something f'r deprecyation. 'Tis about

time f'r whoiver owns me to wurruk me off on a thrust.
Mechanical science has done ivrything f'r me but help
me. I suppose I ought to feel supeeryor to me
father. He niver see a high buildin' but he didn't
want to. He cudden't come here in five days but he
was a wise man an' if he cud've come in three he'd
have stayed in th' County Roscommon.

"Th' pa-apers tells me that midical science has
kept pace with th' hop-skip-an'-a-jump iv mechanical
inginooty. Th' doctors has found th' mickrobe iv
ivrything fr'm lumbago to love an' fr'm jandice to
jealousy, but if a brick bounces on me head I'm crated
up th' same as iv yore an' put away. Rockyfellar
can make a pianny out iv a bar'l iv crude ile, but no
wan has been able to make a blade iv hair grow on
Rockyfellar. They was a doctor over in France that
discovered a kind iv a thing that if 'twas pumped into
ye wud make ye live till people got so tired iv seein'
ye around they cud scream. He died th' nex' year
iv premachure ol' age. They was another doctor cud
insure whether th' nex' wan wud be a boy or a girl.
All ye had to do was to decide wud it be Arthur or
Ethel an' lave him know. He left a fam'ly iv un-
marredgeable daughters.

"I sometimes wondher whether pro-gress is anny
more thin a kind iv a shift. It's like a merry-go-
round. We get up on a speckled wooden horse an'
th' mechanical pianny plays a chune an' away we go,
hollerin'. We think we're thravellin' like th' divvle
but th' man that doesn't care about merry-go-rounds
knows that we will come back where we were. We

get out dizzy an' sick an' lay on th' grass an' gasp:
'Where am I? Is this th' meelin-yum?' An' he
says: 'No, 'tis Ar-rchey Road.' Father Kelly says
th' Agyptians done things we cudden't do an' th'
Romans put up sky-scrapers an' aven th' Chinks had
tillyphones an' phony-grafts.

" I've been up to th' top iv th' very highest buildin'
in town, Hinnissy, an' I wasn't anny nearer Hivin
thin if I was in th' sthreet. Th' stars was as far
away as iver. An' down beneath is a lot iv us runnin' an' lapin' an' jumpin' about, pushin' each other
over, haulin' little sthrips iv ir'n to pile up in little
buildin's that ar-re called sky-scrapers but not be th'
sky; wurrukin' night an' day to make a masheen
that'll carry us fr'm wan jack-rabbit colony to another an' yellin', ' Pro-gress!' Pro-gress, oho! I
can see th' stars winkin' at each other an' sayin':
' Ain't they funny! Don't they think they're playin' hell!'

" No, sir, masheens ain't done much f'r man. I
can't get up anny kind iv fam'ly inthrest f'r a steam
dredge or a hydhraulic hist. I want to see sky-scrap-
in' men. But I won't. We're about th' same hight
as we always was, th' same hight an' build, composed
iv th' same inflammable an' perishyable mateeryal, an
exthra hazardous risk, unimproved an' li'ble to col-
lapse. We do make pro-gress but it's th' same kind
Julyus Cæsar made an' ivry wan has made befure or
since an' in this age iv masheenery we're still burrid
be hand."

"What d'ye think iv th' man down in Pinnsylvanya

who says th' Lord an' him is partners in a coal mine?" asked Mr. Hennessy, who wanted to change the subject.

"Has he divided th' profits?" asked Mr. Dooley.

# Swearing

"DID ye see what th' prisidint said to th' throlley man that bumped him?" asked Mr. Dooley.

"I did not," said Mr. Hennessy. "What was it?"

"I can't tell ye till I get mad," said Mr. Dooley. "Lave us go into ixicutive sission. Whisper. That was it. Ha, ha. He give it to him sthraight. A good, honest, American blankety-blank. Rale language like father used to make whin he hit his thumb with th' hammer. No 'With ye'er lave' or 'By ye'er lave,' but a dacint 'Damn ye, sir,' an' a little more f'r th' sake iv imphasis.

"What else wud ye have him do? 'Twas nayether th' time nor th' occasion, as th' candydate said whin they ast him where he got his money, 'twas nayether th' time nor th' occasion f'r wurruds that wud be well rayceived at Chatauqua. A throlley car had pushed him an' diplomatic relations was suspinded. He was up on top iv a bus, hurryin' fr'm speech to speech an' thinkin' what to say next. 'Th' thrusts,' says he to himsilf, 'are heejous monsthers built up be th' inlightened intherprise iv th' men that have done so much to advance pro-gress in our beloved counthry,' he says. 'On wan hand I wud stamp thim undher fut; on th' other hand not so fast. What I want

[ 223 ]

more thin th' bustin' iv th' thrusts is to see me fellow counthrymen happy an' continted. I wudden't have thim hate th' thrusts. Th' haggard face, th' droopin' eye, th' pallid complexion that marks th' inimy iv thrusts is not to me taste. Lave us be merry about it an' jovial an' affectionate. Lave us laugh an' sing th' octopus out iv existence. Betther blue but smilin' lips anny time thin a full coal scuttle an' a sour heart. As Hogan says, a happy peasanthry is th' hope iv th' state. So lave us warble ti-lire-a-lay—' Jus' thin Euclid Aristophanes Madden on th' quarther deck iv th' throlley car give a twisht to his brake an' th' chief ixicutive iv th' nation wint up in th' air with th' song on his lips. He wint up forty, some say, fifty feet. Sicrety Cortilloo says three hundherd an' fifty. Annyhow whin he come down he landed nachrally on his feet.

"Now, Hinnissy, no matther what a man may've been wan minyit befure he was hit be a throlley car, a minyit afther he's on'y a man. Th' throlley car plays no fav'rites. It bounces th' high an' th' low alike. It tears th' exalted fr'm their throne an' ilivates th' lowly. So whin th' prisidint got back to the earth he wasn't prisidint anny longer but Tiddy Rosenfelt, 180 pounds iv a man. An' he done accordin'ly. If it'd been Willum Jennings Bryan, he'd've ast th' throlley engineer was he a mimber iv th' Union. If he cud show a wurrukin' card he was entitled to bump anny wan. At worst Willum Jennings Bryan wud've written an article about him in th' *Commoner*, or if he felt unusually vindicative,

maybe he'd sind it to him through th' mails. Whin
Sicrety Cortilloo come to fr'm a dhream that he'd
jus' rayfused a favor to Sinitor Tillman, he hauled
out a little note book an' got ready to take down
something that cud be put on th' thransparencies two
years fr'm now—something like—' No power on earth
can stop American business entherprise.' But nawthin' that will iver be printed in th' first reader
dhropped fr'm th' lips iv th' chief exicutive. With
two jumps he was in th' throlley man's hair an' spoke
as follows— No, I won't say it again. But I'll tell ye
this much, a barn-boss that was standin' by an' heerd
it, said he niver befure regretted his father hadn't
sint him to Harvard.

" We know what Wash'nton said to his gin'rals an'
what Grant said to Lee an' what Cleveland said to
himsilf. They're in th' books. But engraved in th'
hearts iv his counthrymen is what Rosenfelt said to
th' throlley man. 'Twas good because 'twas so
nachral. Most iv th' sayin's I've read in books
sounds as though they was made be a patent inky-
bator. They go with a high hat an' a white tie. Ye
can hear th' noise iv th' phonygraft. But this here
jim of emotion an' thought come sthraight fr'm th'
heart an' wint right to th' heart. That's wan reason I think a lot iv us likes Tiddy Rosenfelt that
wudden't iver be suspicted iv votin' f'r him. Whin
he does anny talkin'—which he sometimes does—he
talks at th' man in front iv him. Ye don't hear him
hollerin' at posterity. Posterity don't begin to vote
till afther th' polls close. So whin he wished to

convey to th' throlley man th' sintimints iv his bosom, he done it in wurruds suited to th' crisis, as Hogan wud say. They do say his remarks singed th' hair off th' head iv th' unforchnit man.

"I don't believe in profanity, Hinnissy—not as a reg'lar thing. But it has its uses an' its place. F'r instance, it is issintial to some thrades. No man can be a printer without swearin'. 'Tis impossible. I mind wanst I wint to a printin' office where a frind iv mine be th' name iv Donovan held cases an' I heerd th' foreman say: 'What gintleman is setting A thirty?' he says. 'I am,' says a pale aristocrat with black whiskers who was atin' tobacco in th' rear iv th' room. 'Thin,' says th' foreman, 'ye blankety-blank blacksmith, get a move on ye. D'ye think this is a annyooal incyclopejee?' he says. Ivrybody swore at ivrybody else. Th' little boys runnin' around with type prattled innocent pro-fanity an' afther awhile th' iditor come in an' he swore more thin annybody else. But 'twas aisy to see he'd not larned th' thrade iv printer. He swore with th' en-thusyasm an' inacc'racy iv an amachoor, though I mus' say, he had his good pints. I wisht I cud ray-mimber what it was he called th' Czar iv Rooshya f'r dyin' jus' as th' pa-aper was goin' to press. I cud've often used it since. But it's slipped me mind.

"Swearin' belongs to some thrades,—like printin', bricklayin' an' plumbin'. It is no help at all, at all to tailors, shoemakers, hair-dressers, dintists or au-thors. A surgeon needs it but a doctor niver. It is a great help in unloadin' a ship an' sailor men always

# Swearing

swear—th' cap'n an' mate whin wurruk is goin' on an' th' men befure th' mast at meals. Sojers mus' swear. They'se no way out iv it. It's as much th' equipment iv a sojer as catridges. In vigorous spoort it is niciss'ry but niver at checkers or chess an' sildom at dominoes. Cowboys are compelled to use it. No wan cud rope a cow or cinch a pony without swearin'. A sthrick bringin' up is th' same as havin' a wooden leg on th' plains. Profanity shud be used sparingly if at all on childher—especially girls—an' sildom on women, though I've knowed an occasional domestic: ' Damn ye'er eyes ' to wurruk wondhers in reg-latin' a fam'ly. Women can't swear. They have th' feelin' but not th' means. Westhern men swear betther thin Eastern men though I mus' say th' mos' lib'ral swearers I iver knew come fr'm Boston.

" But it don't do to use pro-fanity th' way ye wud ordin'ry wurruds. No, sir. Ye've got to save it up an' invist it at th' right time or get nawthin' fr'm it. It's betther thin a doctor f'r a stubbed toe but it niver cured a broken leg. It's a kind iv a first aid to th' injured. It seems to deaden th' pain. Women an' childher cry or faint whin they're hurt. That's because they haven't th' gift iv swearin'. But as I tell ye, they'se no good wastin' it. Th' man that swears at ivrything has nawthin' to say when rale throubles come. I hate to hear annywan spillin' out th' valyable wurruds that he ought to save to be used whin th' shtove-pipe comes down. Not that it shocks me. I'm a dimmycrat. But I know th' foolish man is hurtin' himsilf. Put a little pro-fanity by f'r rainy

[ 227 ]

days, says I. Ye won't miss it an' at th' end iv th'
year whin ye renew ye'er lease ye'll be surprised to
find out how much ye have on hand. But if ye hurl
it broadcast, if ivry time ye open ye'er mouth a hot
wan lapes out, th' time will come whin ye'll want to
say something scorchin' an' ye'll have nawthin' to say
that ye haven't said f'r fun. I'd as soon think iv
swearin' f'r pleasure as iv lindin' money f'r pleasure.
They ain't too much pro-fanity in th' wurruld. A
good dale iv it has been used up since th' coal sthrike
begun. Th' govermint ought to presarve it an' pre-
vint annywan fr'm swearin' more thin was niciss'ry
f'r to support life.

" I niver knew Father Kelly to swear but wanst.
'Twas a little wan, Hinnissy. Dhropped fr'm th'
lips iv a polisman it wud've sounded like a ' thank ye
kindly.' But, be Hivins, whin I heerd it I thought
th' roof wud fall down on th' head iv Scanlan that
he was thryin' to show th' evil iv his ways. Melia
Murdher, but it was gran'! They was more varchue
in that wan damn thin in a fastin' prayer. Scanlan
wint to wurruk th' nex' day an' he hasn't tasted a
dhrop since.

" But th' best thing about a little judicyous swearin' is that it keeps th' temper. 'Twas intinded as a
compromise between runnin' away an' fightin'. Befure it was invinted they was on'y th' two ways out
iv an argymint."

" But I've heerd ye say a man was swearin' mad,"
said Mr. Hennessy.

" He wasn't fightin' mad, thin," said Mr. Dooley.

# The War Game

# THE WAR GAME

"WHAT'S this here war game I've been readin' about?" asked Mr. Hennessy.

"It's a kind iv a blind man's buff," said Mr. Dooley. "It's a thrile iv cunnin' an' darin' between th' army an' th' navy. Be manes iv it we larn whether th' inimy cud sneak into Boston afther dark without annywan seein' thim an' anchor in Boston common. Ye an' I know diff'rent, Hinnissy. We know how manny people are in th' sthreets afther dark. But th' navy don't know an' th' army don't know. Their idee is that a German fleet might gumshoe up th' harbor in th' dark iv th' moon an' whin people turned out f'r their mornin' dhram, there wud be th' Impror Willum atin' his breakfast iv Hungayrian Goolash an' noodle soup on th' steps iv th' State House iv Matsachoosetts. But it's a gran' game. I'd like to play it mesilf. It's as noisy as forty-fives between Connock men an' as harmless as a steeryopticon letcher. If war an' th' war game was th' same thing, I'd be an admiral, at laste, be this time with me face gashed an' seamed be raspberry jam an' me clothes stained with English breakfast tea.

"Th' navy chose to be th' inimy an' 'twas th' jooty iv th' navy to divastate th' New England coast. On th' other hand, th' business iv th' army was to catch

th' navy at its neefaryous wurruk an' tag it befure
it cud get its fingers crost. To play th' game well,
th' navy must act as much like an inimy as it can an'
th' army must pretind to be jus' as cross at th' navy
as it is whin they are both on the same side. Frindship ceases whin they set in.

"It's a hard game to follow if ye're lookin' on an'
puttin' up th' money as I am. I've been readin'
about it in th' pa-apers an' I can't make out now
whether th' inimy is lootin' th' breweries iv Conneti-
cut or whether th' definders iv our hearths has blown
thim up in th' harbor iv New London. 'I have th'
honor to rayport,' says Admiral Higginson, 'that I
have this day desthroyed all th' forts on th' New
England coast, put th' definders to rout with gr-reat
slaughter an' kilt with me own hands Gin'ral McArthur th' Commander iv th' lan' foorces—a brave man
but no match f'r ye'ers thruly. His las' wurruds to
me was "Higginson, ye done well!" I rayturned
him his soord with th' wurruds: "Gin'ral, between
two brave men there can be no hard feelin's." Th'
battle in which me gallant foe met his fate was th'
con-clusion iv wan iv th' mos' successful socyal an'
naval campaigns in th' histhry iv our counthry. I
have th' honor to inform ye that promptly on th'
declaration iv war, I give an afthernoon tea to th'
Duchess iv Marlborough. Th' forts at Newport attimpted to reply, but was unable to scoor more thin
three or four westhren millyonaires an' soon suc-
cumbed to th' inivitable. I thin moved up th' Sound
an' fell upon Gin'ral McArthur whin he wasn't

lookin'. Befure he cud load his guns, we poored a perfect blankety-blank hell iv blank catridges on him. He made a spirited reply but t'was useless. We out-fought him be nearly fifty thousan' dollars worth iv powdher. In th' mist iv th' flame an' smoke, I dis-cerned th' caitiff foe standin' on top iv a fort direct-in' his wav'rin' foorces. " Hi-spy, Gin'ral McAr-thur," says I in claryon tones, an' th' battle was over to all intints an' purposes. I have to ispicially com-mind Cap'n McWhallop who, findin' his boat caught between th' fires an' th' inimy, called out: " Lay me down, boys, an' save th' ship. I'm full iv marmy-lade." Th' ladies aboord was perfectly delighted with th' valor an' hospitality iv our men. To-night we completed our wurruk be givin' a dinner an' hop on boord th' flagship. Among those presint was—' an' so on.

" That's what th' gallant Higginson says. But listen to what th' akelly gallant McArthur says: ' I have th' honor to rayport that mesilf an' me gallant men, but largely if I do say it that shudden't, mesilf, crushed an' annihilated th' inimy's fleet at high noon to-day. Las' night at th' first round iv jacks, or midnight, as civilyans wud say, we rayceived a rayport fr'm our vigylant scouts that th' inimy were not at Bar Harbor, Pookypsie, Keokuk, Johannesboorg or Council Bluffs. But where were they? That was th' question. An idee struck me. War is as much a matther iv ingenooty an' thought as iv fire an' slaugh-ter. I sint out f'r an avenin' paper an' as I suspict-ed, it announced that th' craven foe was about two

blocks away. At that very moment, th' sthrains **iv**
th' " Bloo Danoob " was wafted to me ears an' me
suspicions was confirmed. On such occasions there is
no sleep f'r th' modhren sojer. Napolyon wud've
gone to bed but slumber niver crost me tired eyelids.
'Twas six o'clock whin we cashed in an' each wint to
th' mournful jooties iv th' day, silently but with a
heart full iv courage. At high noon, we fell upon
th' inimy an' poored out about eighty-five thousan'
dollars worth iv near-slaughter on him. His guns
was choked with cotillyon favors an' he did not reply
at wanst, but whin he did, th' scene was thruly awful.
Th' sky was blackened be th' smoke iv smokeless
powdher an' th' air was full iv cotton waste fr'm th'
fell injines iv desthruction. A breeze fr'm shore carried out to me ears th' wails iv th' wounded tax pay-
ers. At twelve fifteen, I descried th' bloodthirsty
Higginson—an' a good fellow Caleb is at that—on
th' roof iv his boat. " Hi-spy," says he. " Hi-spy
ye'er gran'mother," says I. " I've had me eye on
ye f'r fifteen minyits an' ye're a dead man as I can
prove be witnesses," I says. An' he fell off th' roof.
I was sorry to take his life but war knows no mercy.
He was a brave man but foolhardy. He ought niver
to've gone again' me. He might've licked Cervera
but he cudden't lick me. We captured all th' men-iv-
war, desthroyed most iv th' cruisers an' ar-re now
usin' th' flag-ship f'r a run-about. Th' counthry is
safe, thanks to a vigylant an' sleepless army. I will
go up to New York tomorrah to be measured f'r th'
prisintation soord."

# The War Game

" There it is, Hinnissy. Who won? I don't know.
I can't tell at this minyit whether I ought to be undher th' bed larnin' German f'r th' time whin a
Prooshyan sojer'll poke me out with his saber, or
down at Finucane's hall callin' a meetin' to thank th'
definders iv th' fireside. Nobody knows. It's a
quare game, f'r they tell me afther th' battles has
been fought an' th' kilt has gone back to holeystonin'
th' deck an' th' smoke fr'm th' chafin' dish has cleared
away, th' decision is up to a good figurer at Wash'n-
ton. It depinds on him whether we ar-re a free people or whether we wear th' yoke iv sarvichood an'
bad German hats f'r all time. He's th' officyal scoorer
an' what Higginson thinks was a base hit, he calls a
foul an' what McArthur calls an accipted chanst is
an error. Afther th' gallant lads in blue an' gold
has got through, a wathry-eyed clerk named Perkins
H. Something-or-other, sets down an' figures out th'
victhry. Th' man behind th' fountain pen is th' boy.
It's up to him whether th' stars an' sthripes still floats
over an onconquered people or whether five pfennigs
is th' price iv a dhrink in New York. He sets on his
high stool an' says he: ' Five times eight is twinty-
nine, subthract three f'r th' duchess, a quarther to
one o'clock an' eighty miles fr'm Narragansett pier is
two-an'-a-half, plus th' load-wather-line iv th' saloon
companionway, akel to two-fifths iv th' differentyal
tangent. Huroo! Misther Sicrety, ye can go home
an' tell ye'er wife th' counthry's safe.' He has to be
a smart man. A good book-keeper, as th' pote says,
is th' counthry's on'y safety. He mus' be careful,

too, d'ye mind. Th' honor iv th' army an' the navy is at stake. Wan or th' other iv thim has been careless."

"D'ye think a foreign fleet cud capture this counthry?" asked Mr. Hennessy.

"Not onless it was op'rated be a throlley," said Mr. Dooley. "Supposin' ye an' I had throuble, Hinnissy, an' both iv us was armed with bricks an' ye was on roller skates an' I was on th' top iv a house, how much chanst wud ye have again' me? Ships is good to fight other ships. That's all. I'd sooner be behind a bank iv mud thin in th' finest ship in th' wurruld. A furrin inimy thryin' to get up to New York wud be like a blind burglar attimptin' to walk on th' top iv a hot-house with all th' neighbors an' th' neighbors' dogs waitin' f'r him. Th' war game is all right. It don't do anny harm. But it's like punchin' th' bag an' I'd jus' as soon thrain a man f'r a fight be larnin' him to play th' mandolin, as be insthructin' him in bag punchin'. It's a fine game. I don't know who won, but I know who lost."

"Who's that?" asked Mr. Hennessy.

"Th' threeasury," said Mr. Dooley.

# Newspaper Publicity

"WAS ye iver in th' pa-apers?" asked Mr. Dooley.

"Wanst," said Mr. Hennessy. "But it wasn't me. It was another Hinnissy. Was you?"

"Manny times," said Mr. Dooley. "Whin I was prom'nent socyally, ye cud hardly pick up a pa-aper without seein' me name in it an' th' amount iv th' fine. Ye must lade a very simple life. Th' news-paper is watchin' most iv us fr'm th' cradle to th' grave, an' befure an' afther. Whin I was a la-ad thrippin' continted over th' bogs iv Roscommon, ne'er an iditor knew iv me existence, nor I iv his. Whin annything was wrote about a man 'twas put this way: 'We undhershtand on good authority that M—l—chi H——y, Esquire, is on thrile before Judge G——n on an accusation iv l—c—ny. But we don't think it's true.' Nowadays th' larceny is discovered be a newspa-aper. Th' lead pipe is dug up in ye'er back yard be a rayporther who knew it was there because he helped ye bury it. A man knocks at ye'er dure arly wan mornin' an' ye answer in ye'er nighty. 'In th' name iv th' law, I arrist ye,' says th' man seizin' ye be th' throat. 'Who ar-re ye?' ye cry. 'I'm a rayporther f'r th' Daily Slooth,' says he. 'Photty-grafter, do ye'er jooty!' Ye're hauled off in th' circylation wagon to th' newspaper office, where a con-fission is ready f'r ye to sign; ye're thried be a jury iv th' staff, sintinced be th' iditor-in-chief an' at tin o'clock Friday th' fatal thrap is sprung be th' fatal thrapper iv th' fam'ly journal.

"Th' newspaper does ivrything f'r us. It runs th' polis foorce an' th' banks, commands th' milishy, conthrols th' ligislachure, baptizes th' young, marries th' foolish, comforts th' afflicted, afflicts th' comfort- able, buries th' dead an' roasts thim aftherward. They ain't annything it don't turn its hand to fr'm explainin' th' docthrine iv thransubstantiation to com- posin' saleratus biskit. Ye can get anny kind iv information ye want to in ye'er fav'rite newspaper about ye'ersilf or annywan else. What th' Czar whispered to th' Imp'ror Willum whin they were alone, how to make a silk hat out iv a wire matthress, how to settle th' coal sthrike, who to marry, how to get on with ye'er wife whin ye're married, what to feed th' babies, what doctor to call whin ye've fed thim as directed,—all iv that ye'll find in th' pa-apers.

"They used to say a man's life was a closed book. So it is but it's an open newspaper. Th' eye iv th' press is on ye befure ye begin to take notice. Th' iditor obsarves th' stork hoverin' over th' roof iv 2978½B Ar-rchey Road an' th' article he writes about it has a wink in it. 'Son an' heir arrives f'r th' Hon'rable Malachi Hinnissy,' says th' pa-aper befure ye've finished th' dhrink with th' doctor. An' afther that th' histhry iv th' offspring's life is found in th' press:

"'It is undhershtud that there is much excitement

in th' Hinnissy fam'ly over namin' th' lates' sign. Misther Hinnissy wishès it called Pathrick McGlue afther an uncle iv his, an' Mrs. Hinnissy is in favor iv namin' it Alfonsonita afther a Pullman car she seen wan day. Th' Avenin Fluff offers a prize iv thirty dollars f'r th' bes' name f'r this projeny. Maiden ladies will limit their letters to three hundherd wurruds.'

" ' Above is a snap shot iv young Alfonsonita Mc-Glue Hinnissy, taken on his sicond birthday with his nurse, Miss Angybel Blim, th' well-known specyal nurse iv th' Avenin' Fluff. At th' time th' phottygraft was taken, th' infant was about to bite Miss Blim which accounts f'r th' agynized exprission on that gifted writer's face. Th' Avenin Fluff offers a prize iv four dollars to th' best answer to th' question: " What does th' baby think iv Miss Blim? " ' '

" ' Young Alf Hinnissy was siven years ol' yisterdah. A rayporther iv th' Fluff sought him out an' indeavored to intherview him on th' Nicaragooan Canal, th' Roomanyan Jews, th' tahriff an' th' thrusts. Th' comin' statesman rayfused to be dhrawn on these questions, his answer bein' a ready, " Go chase ye'ersilf, ye big stiff! " Afther a daylightful convarsation th' rayporther left, bein' followed to th' gate be his janial young host who hit him smartly in th' back with a brick. He is a chip iv th' ol' block.'

" ' Groton, Conn., April 8. Ye'er rayporther was privileged to see th' oldest son iv th' Hon'rable Malachi Hinnissy started at this siminary f'r th'

idjacation iv young Englishmen bor-rn in America.
Th' heir iv th' Hinnissys was enthered at th' ex-
clusive school thirty years befure he was bor-rn.
Owin' to th' uncertainty iv his ancesthors he was also
enthered at Vassar. Th' young fellow took a lively
intherest in th' school. Th' above phottygraft riprisints him mathriculatin'. Th' figures at th' foot
ar-re Misther an' Mrs. Hinnissy. Those at th' head
ar-re Profissor Peabody Plantagenet, prisident iv th'
instichoochion an' Officer Michael H. Rafferty. Young
Hinnissy will remain here till he has a good cukkin'
idjacation.'

" ' Exthry Red Speshul Midnight Edition.
Mumps! Mumps! Mumps! Th' heir iv th' Hinnissy's sthricken with th' turr'ble scoorge. Panic on
th' stock exchange. Bereaved father starts f'r th'
plague spot to see his afflicted son. Phottygrafts
iv Young Hinnissy at wan, two, three, eight an' tin.
Phottygrafts iv th' house where his father was born,
his mother, his aunt, his uncle, Profissor Plantagenet,
Groton School, th' gov'nor iv Connecticut, Chansy
Depoo, statue iv Liberty, Thomas Jefferson, Niagara
Falls be moonlight. Diagram iv jaw an' head showin' th' prob'ble coorse iv the Mumpococcus. Inther-
views with J. Pierpont Morgan, Terry McGovern,
Mary McLain, Jawn Mitchell, Lyman J. Gage, th'
Prince iv Wales, Sinitor Bivridge, th' Earl iv Ros-
lyn, an' Chief Divry on Mumps. We offer a prize
iv thirty million dollars in advertisin' space f'r a cure
f'r th' mumps that will save th' nation's pride.—
Later, it's croup.'

# Newspaper Publicity

" An' so it goes. We march through life an' behind us marches th' phottygrafter an' th' rayporther. There are no such things as private citizens. No matther how private a man may be, no matther how secretly he steals, some day his pitcher will be in th' pa-aper along with Mark Hanna, Stamboul 2:01½, Fitzsimmons' fightin' face, an' Douglas, Douglas, Tin dollar shoe. He can't get away fr'm it. An' I'll say this f'r him, he don't want to. He wants to see what bad th' neighbors are doin' an' he wants thim to see what good he's doin'. He gets fifty per cint iv his wish; niver more. A man keeps his front window shade up so th' pa-apers can come along an' make a pitcher iv him settin' in his iligant furnished parlor readin' th' life iv Dwight L. Moody to his fam'ly. An' th' lad with th' phottygraft happens along at th' moment whin he is batin' his wife. If we wasn't so anxious to see our names among those prisint at th' ball, we wudden't get into th' pa-apers so often as among those that ought to be prisint in th' dock. A man takes his phottygraft to th' iditor an' says he: ' Me attintion has been called to th' fact that ye'd like to print this mug iv a prom'nent philanthropist; ' an' th' iditor don't use it till he's robbed a bank. Ivrybody is inthrested in what ivrybody else is doin' that's wrong. That's what makes th' newspapers. An' as this is a dimmycratic counthry where ivrybody was bor-rn akel to ivrybody else, aven if they soon outgrow it, an' where wan man's as good as another an' as bad, all iv us has a good chanst to have his name get in at laste wanst a year.

Some goes in at Mrs. Rasther's dinner an' some as
victims iv a throlley car, but ivrybody lands at last.
They'll get ye afther awhile, Hinnissy. They'll
print ye'er pitcher. But on'y wanst. A newspaper
is to intertain, not to teach a moral lesson."

" D'ye think people likes th' newspapers iv th' prisint time? " asked Mr. Hennessy.

" D'ye think they're printed f'r fun? " said Mr.
Dooley.

Adventure

"WHAT a life iv advinture I have led, to be sure. I've niver been still a minyit since I cud see an' hear—always on th' go, performin' heeroyc actions on land an' sea. Between th' ages iv eight an' fifteen I bet ye I caught more runaway teams thin all th' park polismen in th' wurruld. I begun with stoppin' th' horses iv a man called Monahan that owned a canal boat an' askin' as a reward that he give me a job dhrivin' th' mule. But I rose rapidly in th' wurruld, an' befure I was fifteen I was dashin' out nearly ivry hour an' nailin' a team iv maddened animals in th' bullyvard an' savin' th' life iv th' pet daughther iv a millyonaire. She usully accepted me young hand in marredge in th' dhrug store. But sometimes whin I needed a top or a kite I took money. I'm ashamed to con-fiss it, but I did. Iv coorse I rayfused th' first offer iv th' plu-thycrat. Whin he thried to crowd wan millyon dollars on me, I give him a look iv scorn an' moved away. He was tur-rbly ashamed iv his onmanly action an' followed me up an' be sharp schamin' managed to get two millyons to me in a way that I cuddn't resint. I think it come in th' shape iv an advance payment on th' dowry.

" At fifteen I quit stoppin' runaway horses as on'y suited to childher. After that I wint in almost entirely f'r knockin' down arnychists as they was about to shoot. I saved th' life iv th' Impror iv Rooshya, an' he was anxious f'r to have me stay at th' coort, but people begun to talk about me an' wan iv th' rile princesses an' I left. On my way home I seized an arnychist jus' as he had raised his pistol again th' Prince iv Wales, an' as a reward he freed Ireland on th' spot. I rayceived an ovation f'r this in Dublin in 1860 or thereabouts, but I disclaimed anny glory, was always willin' to do annything f'r me counthry, wisht them th' best iv luck: gintlemen, I can on'y say, I thank ye, I thank ye, I thank ye.

" Me raycint advintures has been more in th' spoortin' line. I had to give up futball afther winnin' victhry f'r me almy matther f'r four successive years be a suparb run aroun' th' end. F'r a long time I sailed th' cup dayfinder ivry year, an' always won be a sthrategy that no wan but mesilf undherstands. I've killed iliphants an' tigers be th' hundherd, rescooed people fr'm dhrownin' be th' thousan', climbed up th' outside iv a burnin' buildin' an' come down with two or three fine-lookin' ladies in me arms, captured forts, charged armies, knocked out th' wurruld's greatest pugilists with a punch, led revolutions, suppressed thim, an' done it all modestly an' quietly.

" Iv coorse I won't say 'twas always th' spirit iv advinture led me into these gallant acts. If I must tell ye th' thruth I've gin'rally took less intherest in th' advinture itself thin in th' reward. I'm always a little hazy about th' details iv how I saved th' girl fr'm th' rapids iv Niagra whin I can't swim, or how I hap-

[ 248 ]

pened to hit th' tiger in th' eye whin I'm so afraid iv firearms, or how I stopped th' runaway team whin I know that th' other day whin th' milkman's horse broke loose th' best I cud do was run to th' edge iv th' sidewalk an' wring me hands an' yell: "Whoa!" But th' grateful millyonaire is always distinct. I can always hear th' cheers iv th' crowd as I come dhrippin' fr'm th' wather. Though th' raison I happened to be ladin' me rig'mint up th' hill iv San Joon is not clear to me now, I can plainly see mesilf returnin' fr'm th' war, bronzed and weather-beaten, settin' erect on me horse an' respondin' to th' frantic cheers iv th' multichood with a slight bow. I always used to lose an arm or part iv an arm, but I've larned that isn't nicess'ry.

"An' where have all these advintures occurred, d'ye say? Well, some iv th' most feerocyous iv thim happened in me bedroom, an' some on th' front stoop iv th' house on warm moonlight nights, but most iv thim here in this room in front iv th' fire. Be rights th' walls ought to be dic'rated with moose antlers, tigers' heads, diplomas, soords, votes iv Congress, medals an' autygrafted pitchers iv th' crowned heads iv Europe. Th' best advintures anny iv us has is at home in a comf'rtable room—th' mos' excitin' an' th' asiest. Ye can make ye'ersilf as brave as ye want an' as cool, ye avide mussin' ye'er clothes, ye flavor with danger to suit th' taste, an' ye get a good dale more applause an' get it quicker thin th' other kind iv hayro. F'r manny years I've shot all me tigers fr'm this rockin' chair."

# Rights and Privileges of Women

# RIGHTS AND PRIVILEGES OF WOMEN

"WOMAN'S RIGHTS? What does a woman want iv rights whin she has priv'-leges? Rights is th' last thing we get in this wurruld. They're th' nex' things to wrongs. They're wrongs tur-ned inside out. We have th' right to be sued f'r debt instead iv lettin' the bill run, which is a priv'lege. We have th' right to thrile be a jury iv our peers, a right to pay taxes an' a right to wurruk. None iv these things is anny good to me. They'se no fun in thim. All th' r-rights I injye I don't injye. I injye th' right to get money, but I niver have had anny money to spind. Th' consti-chooshion guarantees me th' right to life, but I die; to liberty, but if I thry bein' too free I'm locked up; an' to th' pursoot iv happiness, but happiness has th' right to run whin pursood, an' I've niver been able to three her yet. Here I am at iver-so-manny years iv age blown an' exhausted be th' chase, an' happiness is still able to do her hundhred yards in tin minyits flat whin I approach. I'd give all th' rights I read about for wan priv-lege. If I cud go to sleep th' min-yit I go to bed I wudden't care who done me votin'.

"No, sir, a woman don't need rights. Th' pope, imprors, kings an' women have priv-leges; ordhin'ry men has rights. Ye niver hear iv th' Impror of Rooshya demandin' rights. He don't need thim in

his wurruk. He gives thim, such as they ar're, to th'
moojiks, or whativer it is ye call thim. D'ye think
anny wan wud make a gr-reat success be goin' to th'
Czar an' sayin': " Czar (or sire, as th' case may be),
ye must be unhappy without th' sufferage. Ye must
be achin' all over to go down to th' livry stable an' cast
ye'er impeeral ballot f'r Oscaroviski K. Hickinski f'r
school thrustee?" I think th' Czar wud reply:
' Gintlemen, ye do me too much honor. I mus' rayfuse. Th' manly art iv sufferage is wan iv th' most
potint weepins iv th' freeman, but I'm not used to it,
an' I wudden't know what to do with it. It might be
loaded. I think I'll have to crawl along with me
modest preerogatives iv collectin' th' taxes, dalin' life
an' death to me subjicks, atin' free, dhrinkin' th' best
an' livin' aisy. But ye shall have ye'er rights. Pos-
ieotofski, lade th' gintlemen out into th' coortyard an'
give thim their rights as Rooshyan citizens. I think
about twinty f'r each iv th' comity an' about a dozen
exthry f'r the chairman. F'r wan iv th' rights guar-
anteed to his subjicks, be me sainted father, was a
good latherin' ivry time it was comin' to thim.'

" An' so it is with women. They haven't th' right
to vote, but they have th' priv'lege iv conthrollin' th'
man ye ilict. They haven't th' right to make laws,
but they have th' priv'lege iv breakin' thim, which is
betther. They haven't th' right iv a fair thrile be a
jury iv their peers; but they have th' priv'lege iv an
unfair thrile be a jury iv their admirin' infeeryors.
If I cud fly d'ye think I'd want to walk?"

# Avarice and Generosity

# AVARICE AND GENEROSITY

"I NIVER blame a man f'r bein' avaricyous in his ol' age. Whin a fellow gits so he has nawthin' else to injye, whin ivrybody calls him 'sir' or 'mister,' an' young people dodge him an' he sleeps afther dinner, an' folks say he's an ol' fool if he wears a buttonhole bokay an' his teeth is only tinants at will an' not permanent fixtures, 'tis no more thin nach'ral that he shud begin to look around him f'r a way iv keepin' a grip on human s'ciety. It don't take him long to see that th' on'y thing that's vin'rable in age is money an' he pro-ceeds to acquire anything that happens to be in sight, takin' it where he can find it, not where he wants it, which is th' way to accumylate a fortune. Money won't prolong life, but a few millyons judicyously placed in good banks an' occas'nally worn on th' person will rayjooce age. Poor ol' men are always older thin poor rich men. In th' almshouse a man is decrepit an' mournful-lookin' at sixty, but a millyonaire at sixty is jus' in th' prime iv life to a frindly eye, an' there are no others.

"It's aisier to th' ol' to grow rich thin it is to th' young. At makin' money a man iv sixty is miles ahead iv a la-ad iv twinty-five. Pollytics and bankin' is th' on'y two games where age has th' best iv it. Youth has betther things to attind to, an' more iv thim. I don't blame a man f'r bein' stingy anny

[ 257 ]

more thin I blame him f'r havin' a bad leg. Ye know th' doctors say that if ye don't use wan iv ye'er limbs f'r a year or so ye can niver use it again. So it is with gin'rosity. A man starts arly in life not bein' gin'rous. He says to himsilf: " I wurruked f'r this thing an' if I give it away I lose it." He ties up his gin'rosity in bandages so that th' blood can't circylate in it. It gets to be a superstition with him that he'll have bad luck if he iver does annything f'r annybody. An' so he rakes in an' puts his private mark with his teeth on all th' movable money in th' wurruld. But th' day comes whin he sees people around him gettin' a good dale iv injyemint out iv gin'rosity an' somewan says: ' Why don't ye, too, be gin-rous? Come, ol' green goods, unbelt, loosen up, be gin-rous.' ' Gin-'rous? ' says he, ' what's that? ' ' It's th' best spoort in th' wurruld. It's givin' things to people.' ' But I can't,' he says. ' I haven't annything to do it with,' he says. ' I don't know th' game. I haven't anny gin'rosity,' he says. ' But ye have,' says they. ' Ye have as much gin'rosity as annywan if ye'll only use it,' says they. ' Take it out iv th' plasther cast ye put it in an' 'twill look as good as new,' says they. An' he does it. He thries to use his gin'rosity, but all th' life is out iv it. It gives way undher him an' he falls down. He can't raise it fr'm th' groun'. It's ossyfied an' useless. I've seen manny a fellow that suffered fr'm ossyfied gin'rosity.

" Whin a man begins makin' money in his youth at annything but games iv chance, he niver can become gin'rous late in life. He may make a bluff at it.

## Avarice and Generosity

Some men are gin'rous with a crutch. Some men get the use of their gin'rosity back suddenly whin they ar-re in danger. Whin Clancy the miser was caught in a fire in th' Halsted Sthreet Palace hotel he howled fr'm a window: 'I'll give twinty dollars to annywan that'll take me down.' Cap'n Minehan put up a laddher an' climbed to him an' carrid him to the sthreet. Half-way down th' laddher th' brave rayscooer was seen to be chokin' his helpless burdhen. We discovered aftherwards that Clancy had thried to begin negotyations to rayjooce th' reward to five dollars. His gin'rosity had become suddenly par'lyzed again.

"So if ye'd stay gin'rous to th' end niver lave ye'er gin'rosity idle too long. Don't run it ivry hour at th' top iv its speed, but fr'm day to day give it a little gintle exercise to keep it supple an' hearty an' in due time ye may injye it."

# The End of Things

# THE END OF THINGS

"THE raison no wan is afraid iv Death, Hinnessy, is that no wan ra-ally undherstands it. If anny wan iver come to undherstand it he'd be scared to death. If they is anny such thing as a cow'rd, which I doubt, he's a man that comes nearer realizin' thin other men, how seeryous a matther it is to die. I talk about it, an' sometimes I think about it. But how do I think about it? It's me lyin' there in a fine shoot iv clothes an' listenin' to all th' nice things people are sayin' about me. I'm dead, mind ye, but I can hear a whisper in the furthest corner iv th' room. Ivry wan is askin' ivry wan else why did I die. 'It's a gr-reat loss to th' counthry,' says Hogan. 'It is,' says Donahue. 'He was a fine man,' says Clancy. 'As honest a man is iver dhrew th' breath iv life,' says Schwartzmeister. 'I hope he forgives us all th' harm we attimpted to do him,' says Donahue. 'I'd give annything to have him back,' says Clancy. 'He was this and that, th' life iv th' party, th' sowl iv honor, th' frind iv th' disthressed, th' boolwark iv th' constichoochion, a pathrite, a gintleman, a Christyan an' a scholard.' 'An' such a roguish way with him,' says th' Widow O'Brien.

"That's what I think, but if I judged fr'm expeeryence I'd know it'd be, 'It's a nice day f'r a dhrive to th' cimitry. Did he lave much?' No man is a hayro to his undertaker."

# Hypocrisy

# HYPOCRISY

"IT must be a good thing to be good or ivrybody wudden't be pretendin' he was. But I don't think they'se anny such thing as hypocrisy in th' wurruld. They can't be. If ye'd turn on th' gas in th' darkest heart ye'd find it had a good raison for th' worst things it done, a good varchous raison, like needin' th' money or punishin' th' wicked or tachin' people a lesson to be more careful, or protectin' th' liberties iv mankind, or needin' the money."

# History

# HISTORY

"**I** KNOW histhry isn't thrue, Hinnessy, because it ain't like what I see ivry day in Halsted Sthreet. If any wan comes along with a histhry iv Greece or Rome that'll show me th' people fightin', gettin' dhrunk, makin' love, gettin' married, owin' th' grocery man an' bein' without hard-coal, I'll believe they was a Greece or Rome, but not befure. Historyans is like doctors. They are always lookin' f'r symptoms. Those iv them that writes about their own times examines th' tongue an' feels th' pulse an' makes a wrong dygnosis. Th' other kind iv histhry is a post-mortem examination. It tells ye what a counthry died iv. But I'd like to know what it lived iv."

# Enjoyment

## ENYOYMENT

"I DON'T think we injye other people's sufferin', Hinnessy.  It isn't acshally injyement.  But we feel betther f'r it."

# Gratitude

## GRATITUDE

"WAN raison people ar-re not grateful is because they're proud iv thimsilves an' they niver feel they get half what they desarve. Another raison is they know ye've had all th' fun ye're entitled to whin ye do annything f'r annybody. A man who expicts gratichood is a usurer, an' if he's caught at it he loses th' loan an' th' intherest."